SOP
MOP

CW01082447

Life in the Balance

Lessons Learned in the ER

Hedley Norman Mendez III, M.D.

simply francis publishing company

North Carolina

Dedication

This book would never have been written without the support and love of my wife. Liz and I have been married for fifty years, through all the events in this memoir.

Thanks to Jason Frye, who taught a class at the Osher Lifelong Learning Institute at the University of North Carolina at Wilmington and inspired me to get writing with a deadline. Jason was my first editor. He pointed out many of my rookie mistakes and made good suggestions based on his many years of professional writing.

I also thank fellow writers, whose generous and thoughtful criticism has helped me a lot. Frank Amoroso, Lee Ewing, Shaun Cherewich, and Glenn Taylor read parts of the manuscript, pointing out unclear passages, my improper use of pronouns and some of my many writing "tics." Thanks fellas!

I am also profoundly grateful for the guidance and editing skill of Robert Raleigh. He has challenged me to write more clearly, answering some of the questions the ER cases pose.

Finally, I would be remiss if I didn't thank the many fine nurses and fellow physicians I worked with in the ER. This memoir is my salute to you.

Preface

These stories are what happens in the Emergency Room or ER. They are the product of my thirty-eight years of emergency practice in Virginia and North Carolina. The events and settings are real, although I have changed names to preserve the privacy of individuals. I have also tried to accurately reconstruct conversations from notes I jotted down after working a busy ER shift. My experiences in the ER remain vivid for me, but memories can change with age, so those quickly scribbled notes help this memoir remain true to life.

I also hope to give some insight into how challenging it is to be an ER doctor in today's world of breathtaking medical advances with societal demands that are sometimes overwhelming.

It is my story, starting as a junior medical student, struggling to learn the language of medicine. Strange cases, difficult to crack, were deep mysteries to me as an intern. As a young ER doc, the cases grew harder and in larger number, frequently multiple patients at once. I needed to learn to be objective, to put a distance between me and the patient. This distancing helped to deal with the senseless violence and tragedy, allowing quick thinking and often life-saving actions. As I practiced over the years, recognizing patterns of patient injury and illness, almost without conscious thought, I rediscovered the joy of ER practice becoming comfortable with other people's crises, helping them with skill and kindness. As I reflect on this life in the ER, it is now clear that I have come full circle: growth from a rookie doctor who cared for people without knowing how; the busy ER clinician with many skills, but little time to connect with people; to the seasoned doctor, with all the skills, who cherishes the people he can help in the scary world of the ER.

One of my medical colleagues summed up his feelings succinctly:

"The ER is a nice place to visit, but I wouldn't want to live there!"

Well, that's where I did live for a career, learning and teaching medicine with clinical "stories." Saving some lives, losing some, but caring for all.

TABLE OF CONTENTS

Dedication v

Preface vi

Chapter 1   Gospel 1

Chapter 2   My First Heart Attack 7

Chapter 3   Surgical Scut Boy...13

Chapter 4   Hilda Bryant 19

Chapter 5   Jackson Memorial Hospital ER 25

Chapter 6   Intern on Call 31

Chapter 7   Hampton VA Hospital 41

Chapter 8   USAF Tour of Duty... 47

Chapter 9   My Foolish Pride 55

Chapter 10 MVA (Motor Vehicle Accident) 63

Chapter 11 Cancer 69

Chapter 12 The Knife and Gun Club............................... 79

Chapter 13 Fast-Efficient-Cheap 85

Chapter 14 Snow Day 91

Chapter 15 Frozen Day 99

Chapter 16 House Fire 105

Chapter 17 Spring 109

Chapter 18 A Cough and A Decision 115

Chapter 19 The Hardest Thing 123

Chapter 20 The Smurfettes 129

Chapter 21 The Smurfettes versus Godzilla 133

Chapter 22 Peter Rabbit 139

Chapter 23 Locum Tenens 147

Chapter 24 The Bear... 151

Chapter 25 Misdiagnosis 157

Chapter 26 A Waste of Time 165

Chapter 27 A Man Bitten in the Eye by a Bug 173

Chapter 28 Erin's Smoke Break 181

Chapter 29 Do Dogs Know Grief? 187

Chapter 30 Come Dance with Me 193

Glossary 197

CHAPTER 1
Gospel

It was just after suppertime on a pleasant spring evening in the ER. Our medical team, one ER doc with three ER nurses, had been seeing mostly routine stuff. A few cuts sewn up, a broken wrist splinted and a man with a sinus infection all taken care of and sent home. Then the radio squawked:

"Three victims in shock. Five minutes out."

The paramedic sounded stressed. There were loud background sounds that I couldn't hear clearly. Thoughts and images of traumatized people jumped to mind as I heard this frantic call.

Not that the ER team hadn't dealt with multiple traumas, many times. There was the "case," as one says in dry, clinical terms, of a shoot-out in the Projects. Believe it or not, the medical challenges made that experience positive. Those who arrived alive to the ER would be "salvageable." Simple and straightforward stuff: get the large caliber IV's in, type and crossmatch blood, intubate, take x-rays or CT's, call the surgeon, the Operating Room (OR) and anesthesia. Bing, bang, bong. Patient saved.

I had seen many victims over the years. A woman's face smashed with a brick by her lover. Women beaten unconscious, stripped naked, repeatedly raped, then left under a tree somewhere in the bitter cold. A child thrust into boiling water, because "they cried too much." Infants shaken by baby sitters to quiet them, resulting in brain damage, sometimes death.

Yet, I couldn't remember the paramedics using the term "victims" over the radio before. These first responders are trained EMTs and firemen. They are experienced in tough situations. The tone of the radio call got my heart pounding, and I felt sweat run down my arms and drip off the side of my hands.

The paramedics rolled in the first stretcher. It was a little girl, no more than a toddler whose sweet face was in repose. She gazed up at the ceiling as the paramedics gingerly lifted her tiny body onto the ER stretcher. They are big men, strong men. Yes, even valiant and brave men. They can lay out a hose in the cold, with a blazing house fire making them sweat in their bulky, fire retardant turnout gear. They will crash through an inferno to save your child. But their hard, strong hands trembled as they lifted this child, who was barely more than a baby, maybe three or four years old.

Then the next team brought in the second patient. Also, a child. She looked like the older sister, and you know she will be a head turner. She must have been eight or nine, and very quiet. There were no tears, but I saw pain in her face.

The last patient was a young woman, twenty-nine or so and very thin. She might have been the mother of the children. The paramedics did a two-man lift and put her on the ER stretcher effortlessly. She seemed to settle a bit, like a feather falling to earth. She stared fixedly at the ceiling, not making eye contact with any of us. She must have been in pain from her wounds, but she was mute. There were no tears. She didn't even look at the children. I found that disturbing.

Three severely injured patients on stretchers, awake and alert, making absolutely no sounds was the most baffling scene I had ever witnessed. The paramedics told me of their slipping on all the blood on the floor in the house. It was like a slaughterhouse with blood puddling and sprayed on the wall. But, in front of me were three females, all staring up at the ceiling. It was so quiet it seemed like church, they in open-eyed prayer.

In the ER, many things happen at once. Nurses quickly found that the children had normal pulse rates and blood pressures, so they were not in blood loss shock, yet. The woman had a slightly fast pulse rate and low blood pressure, which needed immediate treatment. The nurses disrobed the patients and got IVs running. I began starting treatment as I puzzled over the cause of the injuries. The questions of What happened to them? Who did this? and Why? stay unanswered for now. As the ER team worked quickly, the smell of blood was strong, almost like tasting a mouthful of copper pennies. It was a frightening and repellent smell, all too familiar in the ER.

The toddler with the sweet, almost beatific stare, had her right hand crudely amputated at the wrist. When arteries are completely transected the muscle lining them reflexively contracts, stopping the hemorrhage. And that is what had saved this little angel. The exposed cut ends of her hand flexor and extensor tendons hang out like spaghetti. The ends of the nerves glistened silver in the harsh overhead spotlights.

I took off her "Sunshine Girl" shirt and found her severed hand wrapped in toilet tissue, next to her belly. I picked it up and asked the nurses to put it into a baggie with sterile saline. I was thinking of the possibility of replantation.

At first glance, I thought the blood on her clothes came from the arm wound, but as I cut off the blood-soaked undershirt, coils of pink intestine bulged out and bled from a nine-inch-long stab wound. Now, I was in a race to save her life. One ER nurse soaked a sterile cloth with saline to cover and protect this belly wound. Another ER nurse had started the IV, sent blood to the lab, and began monitoring vital signs.

The other girl, probably her sister, was quiet through all this activity. The nurses have unclothed her looking for injuries. She also has had her right hand cut off at the wrist. It was wrapped in toilet paper and put under her shirt. The two wrist arteries were spraying in the air with each heartbeat, so I had to stop this or she'll bleed to death. I applied a sterile dressing to the stump of her arm and squeezed with both hands until I saw the blood was seeping, not shooting out. The nurses wrapped this dressing tight with surgical tape and I pulled my hands away. I have bought her time.

I moved to the thin woman, who I believed was the mother. She had not uttered a sound or moved since arrival. She was deaf to what was being said, apparently. The nurses had disrobed her and I saw multiple knife cuts on her left wrist. The left hand was gone. I looked over my shoulder and asked the paramedics to return to the scene and search for the severed hand, cautioning them not to put it on ice, should they find it. Ice would kill tissue and ruin any chance of surgical reattachment. I also asked them to search the garbage, just in case.

There were nineteen incisions on the top of her left wrist and forearm. The exposed tendons were cut fifteen, sixteen times. This was hopeless for any possible reattachment surgery, but I must give her every possible chance for repair. I examined her head to toe, but there were no other wounds. During my exam, the ER nurses had started an IV and sent blood to the lab.

The unit secretary has made the connection I asked for and she called me to the phone. The plastic and general surgeons at our main referral hospital in Norfolk were willing to accept my three "victims" in transfer. The surgeons planned to operate immediately to attempt replantation as soon as I can transfer them.

It took no more than thirty minutes to finish stabilizing and preparing the little girls and their mother for transport.

The nurses and I carefully rolled them to the waiting transport ambulance. The nurses were cooing to the girls. I gently touched the girls on their little foreheads and let my hand brush some stray hair off their faces. I looked down at the little angel and her sister, soon to be a beautiful young lady. I touched the mother's shoulder, too. She seemed not to notice anything that was happening around her.

As I walked back into the ER from the ambulance loading bay, one of the nurses handed me a crumpled slip of paper. It had fallen out of the mother's paper bag of effects. The transport has pulled away, so I looked at it before throwing it away.

It was a grocery store receipt. On the back, scribbled in a crude, childish handwriting was this: "Mt. 5-30."

In the doctor's office, just off the main ER, I had a small desk with a phone. It was a place to make calls to colleagues that offered a bit of quiet and privacy. I sat at the desk chair and pulled out my Bible and opened to the Gospel of St. Matthew, fifth chapter, thirtieth verse. My throat constricted and my eyes welled up as I read:

"And if thy right hand offend thee, cut it off and cast it from thee: for it is profitable for thee that one of thy members should perish and not that thy whole body be cast into hell."

CHAPTER 2
My First Heart Attack

Ernest Evan told me that he drove an eighteen-wheeler "over the road" for a living.

"I been takin' Rolaids for the pain, but it ain't helping. So, I drove myself here to the VA to get something stronger for my stomach."

I was a junior medical student on the medical ward, acting as an intern, with close supervision by Dr. Solomon Papper, a professor of medicine at the University of Miami School of Medicine. Mr. Evans was my very first patient and the doctors in the ER admitted him to me to treat his heart attack.

I introduced myself to him as "doctor," but I don't feel like one. I have been on the medical ward a total of three weeks, learning the way orders are written, what they mean for care of the patient and, most important, who really takes care of patients, the nurses. They have taken me, a lowly med student, under their wings and taught me my first valuable lesson:

"Do not order a bunch of useless stuff!" The nurses know I don't have practical skills and the advice means to be more precise in ordering tests, avoiding the rookie mistake of rote lab testing. "Use a rifle to hit the diagnosis target, not a shotgun," is what they tell me.

Mr. "Call me Ernie" Evans was forty-five years old, heavy set and a cigarette smoker. He was watching me closely and asked, "Can you just give me something better for my stomach?"

I saw a fine bead of sweat on his forehead, even though the air conditioning on the medical ward was almost cold enough to hang meat. His pulse rate was fast and he admitted that he had vomited and was still nauseated. His pain was in the upper part of his belly, or the lower part of his chest, he wasn't sure.

"Sir, you've had a heart attack and you need to stay in the hospital," I said, trying to be professional, but I'm scared. I've got years of book learning and even took a six-week rotation on cardiology, which was only about reading EKGs, but was clueless talking to Ernie now.

I asked the nurses to help me get Ernie into the bed, take his clothes and give him the "johnnie gown" all patients wear. I started the IV, drew blood for the lab and looked up heart attack care in my "portable brain," *The Washington Manual of Medical Therapeutics.*

I confidently ordered Morphine for his pain and Phenergan for his nausea. I am gratified that this helps him.

Now that he was feeling better, I could finish my medical student history and physical. The nurses have guided me to treat the patient before a full examination was done. "Get the patients comfortable and they won't mind answering all your questions," the nurses advised.

Ernie answered that he sometimes drove the truck fourteen to sixteen hours in a row without a break. He had been in the Air

Force as a weapons mechanic, doing heavy work with bombs. He was married and had two kids in elementary school. He ate pork or beef three or four times a week, smoked a pack a day for over twenty-five years. He had a brother who lived upstate and was healthy, as far as he knew. His father died of a heart attack in his early sixties. His mother died from cancer, she was seventy-nine.

I did a complete physical exam, including all the neurologic tests I had read about. I did not do a rectal exam, because I had read in my medical manual that it was not safe to perform in heart attacks. I didn't know the reason for this, but figured the doctor authors knew better than me, a neophyte.

I was feeling less apprehension when I had completed the "H&P" or History and Physical Examination. Then I re-read the section on heart disease and saw that I had missed a major treatment-I hadn't ordered nitroglycerin! So many things to keep in mind, and I had just missed one of the most important.

I called the nurse and asked her to start a nitroglycerin intravenous drip. I admitted I wasn't sure how to order it and she showed me the proper way to write it.

Later that day on rounds, I presented the case to Dr. Papper. He suggested increasing the Morphine, increasing the nitroglycerin, and adding Valium to settle the patient's nerves. He also recommended that I move Ernie to a room away from the clatter and buzzing of the cardiac monitor. Those early cardiac monitors gave a loud, distracting beep for every heart beat and could not be silenced. Those sounds became background noise to the nursing staff but were disturbing to all the patients on the medical ward who were close to the machine.

There were no formal CPR courses and if a patient had a cardiac arrest, we did chest compressions and defibrillation with the big paddles pressed down hard on the patient's chest, waiting for the unit to hum and beep as it slowly charged up. The newer heart drugs were just starting clinical trials and not in general use, but we did have Lidocaine to give intravenously to quiet the chaos of runaway heart beats. I was not sure how much Lidocaine to give and I was afraid of it, having seen it cause grand mal seizures the first time I saw it given in the ER.

Ernie's room was dark when I went in to see him at 6 PM. He had just finished his hospital low fat dinner that the dietician recommended. He wanted to smoke a cigarette. I didn't have any other options for him. The nicotine patches and chewing gum hadn't been invented, so I looked the other way. As he puffed on the cigarette, he seemed to relax and talked about his family.

"I'm worried about my job and not being the man I was before."

He was not the kind of man to share feelings easily, so I listened without interrupting or offering silly advice. He talked and I listened. I heard the fear of disability and worry about his marriage. He finished his cigarette, stubbing the butt out on his Jell-O dish.

"Thanks, Doc, I needed that."

I said good night and drove home, thinking about Ernie's feelings.

I rounded on my patients twice a day, morning and evening. I would stop by Ernie's room after evening rounds just to chat. That's not really accurate, no, I would sit by his bedside just to listen to him for a few minutes.

Over the next three weeks I had several other patients admitted to me, cared for with Dr. Papper's guidance, and discharged home, improved. I learned to see my patients twice a day and always listened to the nurse's opinions and recommendations.

Ernie felt better. Repeat EKGs showed a healed scar on his heart and he wanted to go back to work. I had asked for many consultations to guide me. Cardiology, social service and the dietician had also seen the patient. Dr. Papper thought it was safe to discharge him and follow him in the clinic.

"Doc, I'll eat better, but I don't think I can quit smoking," Ernie told me. I asked him to really try to quit for the sake of his heart. He nodded, but I knew he wouldn't stop. He had put aside the hospital gown and had his work clothes on as we sat together in his room.

"Sir, I hope you can come and see me in the medical clinic in two weeks," I told Ernie. "I want to check your lab tests and blood pressure."

"Doc, I really got to get on the road again to support my family" he replied. "Thanks for everything."

I shook hands with my first heart attack patient and he left the room.

My First Heart Attack

Ernie did not return for any clinic visits and I can understand that. He was concerned about his driving job and had missed work. Taking care of Ernie's heart attack taught me to listen to patient's concerns without commenting or interrupting. His confidence in my care grew as he saw me each day trying to help him. I didn't know what to say to him, so listening was natural for me. Of course, I told him what the tests showed and what Dr. Papper suggested for his care, but it was clear to me that he was counting on me. I learned, first hand, how a doctor's interest in the patient and kind words can help healing.

Chapter 3
Surgical Scut Boy

"**S**cut Boy, get these bloods drawn and sent to the lab!" the snotty intern yelled at me. The rounding group of surgical residents and this surgical intern were standing at the nurse's station, waiting for the attending surgeon to arrive. This insulting demand was this intern's method of elevating himself over the medical students on the surgical service. I felt my face flushing and angry words came to mind, but I was here to learn, not argue. The lesson for me was to control myself and never behave this way to anybody. It was a struggle for me to keep my temper in check, but I was helped when my antagonist turned his wrath at another quaking student. It gave me a bit of breathing space to settle down.

Every junior medical student must take the six-week rotation in general surgery. I felt that this clerkship was a combination of mind-numbing routine drudgery and lectures. As students, we were the lowest of the low on the surgical pecking order. We were tasked with the dirty jobs and our rewards were a few crumbs of clinical knowledge.

We did all the dressing changes, we drew all the morning bloods and were expected to be flunkies in the OR. One of my jobs was 4th surgical assistant in a blocked colon operation. I got to hold the Deaver during the surgery. The stainless steel Deaver retractor has a smooth curved blade to hold the liver out of the surgical field. The handle is slightly curved to prevent slipping. I was at the patient's right shoulder, just to one side of the anesthesiologist and out of the way of the operating residents and the attending surgeon. I could just barely see the incision and nothing of the operation itself. After forty-five minutes of gripping the handle and gently pulling the edge of the liver out of the surgeon's way, my hands were throbbing in pain, but I was afraid of getting shouted at by the surgeon if I let my retractor slip.

I was grateful that this operation was not a liver transplant. Those operations were on the order of eight hours long. A fellow student had fainted in the operating room holding a retractor for four hours without a break. I was told that the surgeons didn't even look up. The student woke up on the operating floor and the nurses kicked him out. He had not eaten or had water all day long. We "scut boys" were considered to be free labor by the surgical service.

Students were to arrive on the surgical wards at 6 AM to draw the pre-operative bloods on every patient. Surgical rounds started at 7 AM and you were expected to attend, always in the rear of the entourage, behind the surgical intern, who was behind the first-year resident, who was behind the second year, who was behind the third year, who was behind the chief resident, who stood next to the attending surgeon. I couldn't hear much of what was said or what operations were planned for the patients whose blood I had just drawn. That was too far above me. It was considered an insult if you interrupted rounds with a question to any of the surgeons.

Surgery was my second clerkship having just spent six weeks as an acting intern on the internal medicine wards, so I had some clinical knowledge and was eager to learn surgery. I began by reading the entire textbook of surgery and reading the patient charts. I had a lot of questions and needed to find guidance. One of the younger attending surgeons was tasked with teaching the students. After seeing how a fellow student's question at one of the lectures was dismissed as "stupid," the message was sent to all of us. Just shut up and do the menial tasks without comments.

In the second week, I taught myself how to draw blood and start IVs on anything with a pulse. I also learned how to suture using both one hand and two hand knot tying. One night the service was short-handed and a surgical intern asked me to scrub in on an appendectomy. He showed me how to do a proper incision and how to deliver the hot appendix to the surface for removal. He showed me how to do a purse string suture tie to close the colon after he cut away the diseased appendix. We did the entire case in fifteen minutes. The young patient sailed through the operation. His name was Neal and was about my age. We talked each morning as I changed his dressings. I had only seen him in the OR as a belly with a hot appendix. He felt much better and was eating the next day. I examined his suture line. It was healing with no sign of infection. This "scut boy" had a sense of pride: I had done something good with my scalpel and suture.

Neal healed well and I took out his sutures when I saw him a week later in the surgical clinic.

Helping the surgical intern operate and cure Neal gave me a sense of purpose. I could take the "scut boy" and the necessary day-to-day drudgery since I now knew what surgery was about.

Students had to take ER "call" alongside the house staff. The surgical ER was always overwhelmed with patients. Everybody pitched in to take care of the lacerations, abscesses, and gunshot wounds pouring into the ER. One of the third-year surgical residents complimented me on suturing a complex wound and asked me to help him. I followed him into the trauma room and gloved up.

Suzy was a petite teenager who was rushed to the ER from a party. Someone had stabbed her. She was not breathing and her pupils were dilated. I was sure she was dead but held her head and began pushing air into her mouth and lungs with the resuscitation Ambu bag.

The nurse cut away Suzy's blood- soaked shirt. The front of her chest had been deeply cut. The horrible words that occurred to me was that she had been cleaved in two.

The surgeon asked for a chest retractor, which is a set of curved blades with a gear mechanism at the bottom. He quickly inserted the closed retractor into the wound and cranked hard, ribs snapping and cracked. The nurses began pouring Betadine over the chest and it splashed onto me and the floor.

I could see that Suzy's heart was quivering in the pericardial sac and there was blood oozing from the cut chest wall arteries. Her lungs would move into the surgical field with every puff I gave. The blood was bright red, meaning that the lungs were clearing the body of carbon dioxide. Maybe she had a chance to survive.

The surgeon grabbed a curved scissor off the trauma tray and cut the pericardium, the sac confining and protecting the heart. There was an immediate gush of blood clots onto the floor. I could see that there was a large laceration down the front of the heart, which was quivering, not pumping blood. He called for "four O silk on a cutting needle" and the nurse threaded the silk and handed the needle holder. The surgeon took careful "bites" with the needle and did one hand ties as the nurse handed him one after another silk sutures.

Seven black knotted sutures put the heart back together. He drew out the clotted blood and air from the heart and pushed in sterile saline using a large syringe. He started squeezing the heart to get it to work again. This seemed to take an eternity. Suzy's heart started and the surgeon then sutured the small chest wall arteries that were spurting, now that circulation had begun again.

One of the nurses took the Ambu bag from me and began pushing air into Suzy's lungs. I got on the surgeon's left side, looked at him and rotated the gear on the chest retractor and removed it from her chest at his head nod. The surgeon then sutured the chest laceration as I pushed Suzy's chest together. I took the scissors off the tray and cut the ends of each suture as he tied the knots.

The anesthesiologist had come down to the ER and incubated Suzy. The nurses then rolled her to the Operating Room, where the cardiac surgical team would do a careful revision of the ER work using the surgical microscope and very fine, vascular surgical sutures. The surgeon, the nurse and I exchanged looks as they rushed our patient to the OR. In that quick, silent exchange, I knew we were offering prayers for little Suzy.

I dragged home after fourteen hours of straight suturing in the ER. I was exhausted but also exhilarated. The immediate results I experienced in the ER that night made a lasting impression on me.

I had no further responsibility for Suzy, but I wanted to know what happened to her. Reading her chart in the Intensive Care Unit (ICU) and asking the nurses about her, I filled in the rest of the story.

After the ER, Suzy was taken to the OR and her chest was

opened again to search for other structures damaged by the knife that had cut her heart. The operative report detailed repair of the vagus nerve, laying in front of the heart. The left main coronary artery, which nourished the heart muscle, had been severed and repaired. The surgeons used the operating microscope to tie the cut ends of the artery together.

Her chest wall was wired together and chest tubes placed to drain off air and blood. She had had a total of eight units of blood transfused and left the OR with medicines to maintain her blood pressure and treat for irregular heartbeats.

Every night after my other chores on the surgical ward and OR, I would spin by the ICU to see how Suzy was. The nurses were worried about her, since Suzy never regained consciousness after the surgery.

On the third night, I went to the ICU and the nurses told me that Suzy's blood pressure had bottomed and would not respond, despite maximum efforts. The surgeon pronounced her dead that evening.

I drove home feeling sad. This fifteen-year-old never woke up. I learned that what we had tried in the ER to save her, was "heroic." I didn't feel very heroic at all. I felt more a sense of failure. Of course, that was irrational, based on the hopelessness of Suzy's massive injuries. A physician's feelings about his or her calling, especially in the ER, are irrational, in the very best sense of the word.

Several months later, I read in the paper that her wrongful death was considered murder, but no one was ever caught. The party-goers where she was stabbed told the police that they heard nothing and saw nothing.

Chapter 4
Hilda Bryant

I bet you've burned your fingers on a hot pan, or maybe hot water, or grease splashing onto your arm. Have you had a sleepless night, tossing and turning with sunburn? If so, then you know the pain of burns. Unpleasant, but usually the pain stops as the burned skin heals in a few days.

Hilda's burns were severe and required intensive care in the University of Miami Jackson Memorial Hospital Burn Unit. Working in one of these burn centers takes special dedication day in and day out to help these victims.

Victims of house fires, victims of gasoline dumped on a charcoal grill to start it, victims of chemical explosions, victims of playing with fireworks, children who will never again play with matches. And people who burn other people, deliberately.

Hilda had been set on fire by her husband. She was now twenty-six years old, the mother of two young children. The police summary of her attack one year ago was on her chart and we junior medical students read it in horror. "Hilda Bryant, aged twenty-five, was found by fire rescuers responding to a fire in the fourteen hundred block of North Miami. Her children told rescuers that their father, Silas J. Bryant, age forty-one, had poured gasoline on their mother and set her on fire. He carried the children, ages seven and nine, out of the apartment to the street, where Dade County Police arrested him. The children were put into foster care."

The Burn Unit of Jackson Memorial took up an entire ward of fifteen beds and every single student in my medical school class helped care for each of those patients. But Hilda stands out in my memory forever.

Along with two other classmates, I helped the nurses take Hilda from her hospital room to the whirlpool baths, which helped remove dead skin to prevent infection. After we gently placed her into the lowering harness and dipped into the water, we had to gown, mask, and glove up to start the debridement of the skin. Debridement means to cut away dead or contaminated tissue from a wound. I can remember having trembling hands as I tried to cut away the burned skin. The nurse told us to trim the areas to get down to fresh skin.

"You'll know when you get down to good tissue, it will bleed," she instructed.

I considered the patient's eyes as I tried to be gentle. She grimaced but didn't speak or move as I· clumsily trimmed blackened flesh tags off, dropping them into the whirlpool water.

Hilda was the first patient any of us had seen with such extensive burns, estimated at 60% of her body surface area. The estimate of the extent of her burn was by the "rule of nines." It is medical shorthand to record the extent of a burn to guide immediate fluid resuscitation treatment. The head is 9%, the chest is 18%, the back is 18%, each arm is 9%, each leg is 18%, and the groin is 1% of the body surface area.

In Hilda's case, her hair was burned away, leaving a deeply

scarred face and scalp. She had no eyelids and her lips were drawn up into a caricature of a smile. The front of her body had multiple skin grafts in various stages of healing. Her skin had a pattern of red, freshly grafted patches, blackened charred areas and white, healed grafts. It looked like a crazy quilt with no pattern or design. Her buttocks and upper thigh skin was unburned and became the donor sites for her skin grafts. The healthy skin had been cut in thin slices with the surgical dermatome, which looked like the tool chefs use to thinly slice truffles, and then carefully placed to cover the burned area. Most, but not all of these transplants lived to replace her dead skin, meaning that she had to undergo hundreds of these skin grafts over many months. Her hands and arms were pulled into clenched fists and flexed arms when she first was brought to the burn unit. She had endured multiple operations to release the scars that bound her arms and trapped her fingers.

When my fellow medical students and I helped in Hilda's care she was well along in the healing process. She had endured all those operations and now had to endure the continued debridement. Many of the skin nerves were growing back, making every touch painful, especially when we cut into healthy skin in our inexperienced efforts.

We all thought the attending surgeon was cruel because of his unbending rule that she was to get no narcotics for the painful debridement we had to put her through. The nurses told us that his reasoning was that Hilda had become tolerant to narcotics she had had before, and had demanded increasingly large doses to get relief. As a young medical student, I had no notion of narcotic addiction or how to control a patient's distress. I was troubled by this decision because I feared giving more pain to a woman who has suffered, and now I would have to give her more pain. I had read that a physician should be objective in the care of the patient, but I was not objective at all.

Every morning at 7 AM, I lined up in the hall of the Burn Unit Service with the other students to get our paper gowns on. I stood on one leg and snapped on the shoe protectors. Next came hairnets, facemasks, and gloves. I got good at donning this gear, usually taking only about a minute to transform into a semi-surgeon.

Next, we entered the room and greeted the patient. She had had some breakfast by then. Some days Hilda would nod at us, some days she would just glare, her brown eyes furious at an unwelcome intrusion. She was quiet as we tried to get a blood sample from the veins in her burned arms. She endured the efforts of the bumbling medical students as a minor daily irritant.

Every surface in Hilda's room was stained black. The floor, the bed frame, even the bed linens were deeply stained from the silver nitrate solution that had been applied to her skin over the months. I could never get the black stains out of my pants, socks or shoes, despite the gown and shoe protectors, but I knew that the solution had prevented the dreaded lethal staphylococcal infection. Our skin is an excellent barrier to many pathogens, if the skin is burned, it cannot protect the person. Antibiotics are given when an infection has started, but they are not a dependable cure. Burn specialists know it is more effective to prevent, rather than treat infection.

Hilda must have been half out of her mind most of the time. I helped the nurses get her out of bed for her daily weights and to the potty chair. The blood tests showed that her body was healing.

On the days when I helped take her for physical therapy or to the whirlpool, she begged us for morphine. She must have known we were under strict orders not to give morphine. In those times she cursed us generally, but kept her worst curses for the Attending Surgeon, our boss. The hatred boiled off her as she spat: "That bastard doan care if I die in pain, that sorry motherfucker, I hope that shithead die!"

It was the most agitated any of us had seen and it startled me. I was scared by the vehemence and the bitterness she expressed. I knew that my pathetic efforts to help Hilda did nothing to stop the suffering and I felt ashamed. I had faith in all those big books I had to learn from, and now was beginning to see that I didn't know much at all. I couldn't detach myself from her suffering and I didn't want to become a cold fish, either. I had reached a crisis in my soul. I did not have emotional balance. Somehow, I would have to find this balance of professional detachment and caring. Every doctor and nurse in the healing arts faces this emotional challenge on a daily basis. I also knew, deep down, that it would take a lifetime of trying to get there.

Several months later I heard that Hilda was finally discharged to a skilled nursing home. The Burn Unit social worker told me that her children had been placed in the home of Hilda's sister and brother-in-law, to be raised with their cousins.

The social worker said, "I think Hilda kept living to kill the drunken husband who had set her on fire, but he got arrested and convicted for what he did to her. He is in Starke prison for life, with no chance for parole. I informed her of the conviction. She listened and wept, I couldn't say if it was tears of sadness or anger.

Chapter 5
Jackson Memorial Hospital ER

As a senior medical student, I had completed all the required clerkships of the junior year and now could sample any other area as an elective. The American Board of Medical Examiners part one, a test of all the basic science taught in the first two years of medical school, was in my rear-view mirror. Passing part two, full of clinical questions, was a final hurdle to be cleared before graduation and getting the M.D. degree. The final, and most difficult, part three, must be passed after the first post-graduate year, the internship. Successfully passing all three parts allows the young doctor to take the smallest step for national professional recognition. Then, of course, the state licensure examination had to be passed before medical practice could begin. But passing all three parts of this national test was a badge of honor.

I planned my senior year elective clerkships to fill in some gaps and learn something about the specialties not covered in my junior year. I did clerkships in Ophthalmology, Neurology Stroke service, Ear, Nose, and Throat, Dermatology, Psychiatry, Radiology, and in the ER.

Many of my classmates had decided on a specialty and were sending out resumes to hospitals for applicable training. I was in a quandary as I liked each of the many fields of medicine and surgery, and couldn't narrow my interests. I had been told that the Department of Internal Medicine would accept me for an internship, so that settled it for me. Knowing that, I decided to get as much experience in all the other areas before the internship began.

I had been in the Jackson Memorial Hospital ER several times to accept admitted patients to medicine or surgery but didn't have a feel for what it was like day-to-day. The JMH ER was a large complex, taking up the entire first level of the hospital, about 150,000 square feet in area. It was divided into four main sections, with a large medical ward adjacent to the surgical ward. There was a smaller pediatric and OBG section, and Ward D. Ward D was the Dade County Prison Ward. Inmates who were sick or injured where cared for by the house staff, the interns, and residents.

At 6:30 PM I arrived at the medical side of the ER and introduced myself. This would be my first night shift in the ER. The night team was seated at the long nurse's station desk and I could see the chart rack was full, meaning that there were twenty-five patients present. My boss for this twelve-hour night shift was a first-year resident, only two years ahead of me in training. The team consisted of one first year, one intern, a senior medical student, three nurses, and two nursing assistants. I picked up one of the charts and went into a cubical to see my first patient. He was in the ER for "bleeding." At least that is what the harried front desk clerk had written down as "chief complaint" on the patient's chart. The nursing assistant had taken his blood pressure, pulse rate, and oral temperature, carefully entering the numbers on the chart. The chart was then placed in the chart rack with a little red flag, a clue to the doctors that this was a serious patient and should be immediately seen.

His name was Juan Clasca and he spoke no English. The clerk had no more information beyond his name that she had seen on an old hospital ID bracelet on his thin wrist, and the "bleeding," which she had seen with her own eyes. Relatives had abandoned him in the ER waiting room and vanished. Not an unusual occurrence in Dade County, where dictator Fidel Castro had sent all the criminals, chronically ill, and handicapped Cubans to Miami. Castro's communist regime expropriated all the wealth of the middle class, most of whom arrived in Florida as penniless refugees. These refugees who spoke little or no English, were burdened with chronically ill relatives, so they carried them into the ER waiting room and fled.

The patient was vomiting bright red blood into the waste can. He looked up at me and the yellow sclera of jaundice was easy to see. He had a thin, malnourished face, and a mouth of broken teeth stained with blood and clots. His abdomen was distended with prominent veins, the spider pattern seen with advanced liver cirrhosis. His skin was sallow, and his fingernails were curved and pale, signs of malnutrition and anemia. He mumbled his name as I introduced myself. His speech was incoherent, and he didn't understand my questions in the Spanish I had learned on the wards. I had never studied the language formally, but had a good working knowledge of the language spoken by my Cuban patients. His hands and arms made a curious flapping, like he was a bird trying to fly out of the ER. I had seen this pattern of liver failure, with poisoning of the brain with ammonia. The ammonia produced by our metabolism is normally removed by the liver, but Señor Clasca's liver was very damaged. Sandy, the night nurse had seen me go into the room and brought an IV set up and a liter bag of sterile saline. I got the IV started and drew blood. The blood in the tubes was watery, more pink than red. I knew from his physical appearance and the vomited blood that this was a bleeding ulcer or bleeding varices. The patient with alcoholic cirrhosis has distended veins, varices, at the bottom of the esophagus that can bleed a lot. Sandy and I got the patient to swallow a thin latex tube, passed through the nostril to the stomach. I then began ice water lavage, irrigating the stomach, clearing clots and trying to slow down the bleeding. Most times this helped and, in his case, the bleeding slowed down. I kept putting ice water in and pulling blood tinged water out. Sandy took the chart, made out the lab specimen labels, and sent the tubes to the lab via pneumatic tube. The resident called the admitting team as I was starting a blood transfusion. The team came to the ER to accept the admission. The admitting resident knew the patient from a previous admission for the same complaint.

I was stunned when, in front of the patient, he told me, "These alcoholics either die of bleeding or liver failure. I bet this one will bleed to death."

I was dismayed to hear this. But after five or six similar patients over the next week, I understood his frustration and I, too, became abrupt and callous when dealing with these self-destructive patients. They were helpless to change the alcohol drinking that caused the liver cirrhosis. They never got much better and were the most worrisome type of patient: "the bounce-back." Hospital discharge on a Monday, back in the ER Friday and into the hospital for the same issue. Their care posed a dilemma for the ER. What can we do for them? What is the best disposition?

Disposition meant having to convince the overworked medical team to accept that admission. There were four admitting teams, each team consisting of a resident and two interns. I had to "sell the case." Always, there was push back.

"Send him home, the bleeding always stops!" was the suggestion I received with the alcoholic vomiting blood. I reminded the intern that I had already set up blood to be transfused. Emergency blood transfusion was always reason enough for hospital admission, and he knew it. I suspect that he wasn't thinking clearly due to exhaustion. Or he had "compassion fatigue," feeling frustrated at the lack of meaningful progress.

I had learned one of the most important lessons in emergency medicine. The lesson convincing admitting doctors of the need to accept an "undesirable patient." I had to search my own heart for bias against certain patient types. With Señor Clasca I was seeing in myself a prejudice that was shameful.

In Señor Clasca's case I observed the stigmata of chronic liver failure and knew what the life-threatening complications were. Since he was unable to give any history of his illness and there were no relatives present, it was critical for me to act as his advocate. Many times, in the years to come, the skill to act to save a life, with little or no medical history, would be vital, and treating Señor Clasca now was such a time.

The blood transfusions maintained his blood pressure and heart rate, but he now started bleeding from the venipuncture site. His damaged liver could no longer produce the clotting proteins that would halt the bleeding, so I ordered intravenous vitamin K and transfusion of platelets, the blood cells needed for normal clotting. After several hours, the oozing of blood from the venipuncture stopped and the ice water lavage of his stomach showed a change from bright red blood to pink colored water. I had been able to stop this hemorrhage, but the next challenges were apparent soon. He developed alcohol withdrawal seizures, the most serious complication of delirium tremens, the DT's. I pushed drugs to stop the seizure, knowing that his damaged liver would not be able to metabolize them normally.

I had no good options for Señor Clasca. Seizures would kill him and the drugs to treat those seizures would further damage his liver and kill him.

I had to intubate him when he stopped breathing after the drugs were administered. He was never able to breath on his own. The modern advances of liver transplantation were many years in the future, too late for Señor Clasca. He died of total liver failure soon after hospital admission.

I knew I had done my best. I had experienced treating a critical patient with little or no history. The skills I learned with treating Señor Clasca would be vital in my future.

This JMH ER clerkship was the beginning of a career in emergency medicine, and the challenge of caring for every patient in a compassionate way, especially treating those patients deemed "undesirable" by others.

Chapter 6
Intern on Call

I had just gotten to sleep when the phone startled me awake. It was my third night in a row on call as the intern member of admitting team three at Jackson Memorial Hospital in Miami, Florida, and I'm exhausted. It's the ER calling, so I roll out of bed and stumble to the phone.

"You better get down here. This guy's bleeding pretty good."

I thought, "Oh boy, I really need another "horrendoma," a complicated medical case. I had already gotten three other complex patients and it was only 11 PM and I had another eight hours to go on this shift. The team had twenty-five admitted ward patients as well as these new admissions to round on. I'd been awake, kind of, for thirty hours stumbling through rounds.

Jackson Memorial Hospital is the largest hospital in Dade County and the main teaching hospital for the University of Miami School of Medicine. I had graduated the prior year and knew my way around the hospital but was still intimidated by the ER. It is enormous. One hundred beds divided into medical, pediatric, surgical, orthopedic and the wonderful

Ward D, as in detention. Ward D was the Dade County Jail Unit. That's where the house staff got a lot of experience suturing wounds.

I saw our new patient sitting on the stretcher with a bloody handkerchief pressed to his nose. I examined him and found blood dripping from his nose, mouth, and gums. He had big, irregularly shaped splotches over his chest, back, and legs. The yellow and brown splotches looked like old bruises, while the black and blue ones looked new to me. His rectal exam showed reddish, stringy stool, which tested positive for blood.

I introduced myself and he told me his name, between nose blowing.

"I'm Charles D'Antonio, and I never have been sick before."

I was so tired that I secretly hoped to find rectal hemorrhaging so I could "turf" him over to the general surgical side of the ER, but I couldn't, so, I "owned" him. I started an IV in his arm and at the same time filling blood tubes to go to the lab. The blood looked "watery," no other way to put it, like cherry Kool Aid.

I sent his blood samples to the lab, hoping for a quick answer for the patient's multiple bleeding areas. Maybe it was a leukemia, where the bone marrow was fooled into making only white blood cells, not making the red blood oxygen carrying cells or the platelets, vital to normal blood clotting. If that proved to be the case, then I could get a quick consultation with the Oncology Service, and, maybe they'd take Mr. D'Antonio off my hands.

I asked him a few questions about any medicines he took or

previous surgery.

"Doc, I've been the picture of health until a few weeks ago. I got tired mowing the yard and had to get my breath before finishing up. Then, when I had a nose bleed one day last week, I went to my GP, and he couldn't find anything wrong. He told me it was a sinus infection. He prescribed some antibiotics which I finished taking and they seemed to help. The nosebleed stopped, but I still felt tired all the time."

This could be a cancer in the sinus cavities. Perhaps I could transfer him to the Ear, Nose and Throat surgeons. I had finished a senior year elective clerkship on ENT and was impressed by the skill of the surgeons operating on cancers. They have vast experience with unusual malignancies and in my tired state, I hoped that Mr. D'Antonio would be ENT's case.

All these thoughts were dreams. He was my patient and I better figure out what to do pretty quickly, or he might bleed to death. I had sent all his blood work to the lab STAT, medical code signaling a life and death issue.

I got a phone call from the lab reporting a very abnormal pro-time, short for prothrombin time, a test that screens for blood disorders.

"It's about three times normal, what medicine is he taking?" was the question the hematology technician asked me.

"I don't know that he is on anything. The patient told me that he doesn't even take aspirin. Could you have tested some other patient's blood by mistake?" I said.

The technician was sharp enough to have considered that question and had rechecked the name on the blood tube.

"Is your patient Charles D'Antonio, ID number 436789?" he asked me.

"Yes, that's my patient." I agreed and was even more confused.

The Pro-time test looks for prothrombin in the blood. Prothrombin is the precursor to thrombin. In our bodies thrombin sticks to platelet cells to form a blood clot. No prothrombin means no thrombin. No thrombin means no blood clotting and continuous bleeding, especially into the skin, hence black and blue bruises all over. The lab technician had confirmed that he had normal platelet count and normal red and white blood cells, so my leukemia diagnosis was ruled out.

It didn't seem likely that I could transfer him to Oncology tonight. As I thought about the bleeding and bruising in his skin as well as the nosebleed, my dream of sending him to Ear, Nose and Throat surgery also evaporated.

Dr. Papper always cautioned his students not to overthink medical diagnosis:

"Listen carefully to the patient. The diagnosis is always in the medical history, if you'll just allow the patient the chance to tell you what is wrong with him."

My mentor's words came to me as I went on the ward to see Mr. D'Antonio with the abnormal pro-time test. I was not certain what I would say, so I just stated the facts and let him respond.

"Sir, the lab called me and you have an abnormal prothrombin test."

I could see that he was stunned by this. His face registered confusion and he quickly replied,

"What does this mean? Am I gonna die?"

"I am not sure why you have it. The test means that your blood is not clotting as it should, and it is serious, but you are in the right place to have it. No, you're not going to die. But I need to know if there's anything different in your life to explain why this has happened so recently." I said, trying to express confidence that I really didn't have.

The patient told me that he had always been healthy until a week ago when he was "tired all the time." He denied taking any blood thinners, aspirin or other drugs. He worked for an insurance agency and had no toxic exposure. He drank an occasional beer, but never to excess. He is married and had never missed a day of work in ten years.

All of this added up to a big nothing. I was in a fog and the thought that this still must be a cancer seemed right. I was not thinking clearly and was still hatching a plan to transfer him to Oncology in the morning. I was so tired that all I could do was sleepwalk through writing orders on his chart.

Now, it is known that these brutal, excessive work shifts are bad for patients as well as detrimental to the health of the interns and residents. No one thinks clearly when sleep deprived and hungry. It is a form of torture masquerading as training, but here I was.

I had two more ER calls after tucking him into the ward, so I was dead on my feet when our admitting team dragged into Morning Report at 7 AM. All three of the teams stumbled into the small auditorium and pulled up hard backed folding chairs. Each team had to present a case that had been admitted last night.

My head was nodding when it was my turn to present the bleeding man's case.

The chief medical resident and the attending chief physician were seated at the front on comfortable chairs, legs crossed as they grilled the trembling interns speaking before them. They were fresh, wearing the starched long white lab coats which are the mark of superior authority in our world.

I, like all my fellow lowly interns, wore a short white coat, rumpled and bulging with pens, notebooks, and medical guidebooks. I hadn't showered, shaved, or changed clothes in the last two days of being on call and looked like a hobo impersonating a doctor. Looking around the room I saw a distinct lack of personal grooming, we all looked beat.

Most of us also dreaded Morning Report. It was a tense ass-kicking session, where the Chiefs relished turning the quivering intern into a bowl of Jell-O. These sessions began many years ago as learning opportunities for young trainees to absorb the wisdom regally dispensed from on high. In my years at Jackson, it had become a gauntlet to be run.

Now, it was my turn in the barrel. I described the patient's history and physical exam. I had written some of the lab results on a small file card in my pocket. I read the test results to the group and I had that sinking feeling that I had left something out, but just couldn't think what it could be.

My case got everyone's attention. The attending chief physician was a hematologist, a specialist in bleeding diseases, who peppered me with questions. The gist of which was my failure to get a full hematological lab panel. He demanded that an "adequate" workup would include: this exotic fancy test, that arcane fancy test, and finally the most obscure fancy test known only to the chosen few! I guess I could name the tests but couldn't for the life of me know how to make sense of any results. I was made to feel like a knucklehead for not ordering all these blood tests in the middle of the night. Oh, well, my turn to be Jell-O!

After what seemed like an eternity, suddenly it was over. I felt like I had been released from prison. Our team had been on its feet constantly for thirty-six hours. We were zombies.

I have no memory of walking to the distant parking lot, driving home, or walking up the stairs to our apartment. After one other grueling shift, I had fallen asleep at the dinner table and almost dove into my steaming bowl of soup.

At half past six the following morning, we had our team meeting on the ward to plan our day. The team leader and first year resident, had taken his own H&P (History and Physical) on the "bleeding guy," and he didn't think it was a blood cancer, which had been my working diagnosis.

The team leader had ordered vitamin K for the patient while I had been snoozing on my feet. I should have done that but missed it, being brain dead and exhausted. Fatigue had blotted out my usual thoroughness, an important lesson in humility for me. How many other blunders would I make in the future when exhausted like this?

I repeated the blood test and the pro-time was now almost normal. The patient was anemic and I ordered a blood transfusion to correct that. A plan was forming to just fill the tank and send him home for outpatient follow-up. Clearly this was not a blood cancer. I had that wrong, but what was it? We didn't know, so we were calling it "mysterious anticoagulant, cause unknown." Not a satisfying state of affairs at all.

As he was getting the transfusions he had a visit from his wife. She had brought him his favorite chocolate milkshake. I saw the empty carton in the trash when we saw him on our morning rounds. I drew his blood after he finished the transfusion and sent the specimen to the lab.

An hour later the lab called in alarm. His prothrombin test was sky high again. I couldn't believe it. Could he have confused the samples? Was he sure the test was from today? He read the date on the request and asked me my name to confirm. It was a true sample from today.

I immediately went back to the patient and quizzed him. Had he taken any pills? He was curious, "Why do you doctors keep asking me that? I don't take pills, haven't had to take even an aspirin my whole life. What's going on with me?"

That's what baffled the whole team and me. The team leader told us of a curious case of Munchausen Syndrome he had heard about. That's when people will fake illness, usually to get sympathy and affirmation, but you must be insane to risk bleeding to death just to get attention. Our "bleeding guy" didn't fit that profile. But it had to be considered.

We asked the nurses for help. Did they see anything that might explain these wacky blood tests? Was the patient sneaking drugs to stay sick? The nurses had not seen that happen. Has he been eating or drinking anything different?

"He really craves chocolate milk shakes, he jokes with us. He says it's too bad our cafeteria doesn't have'em."

After the patient had yet another nosebleed, we got suspicious of those milk shakes. We'd ruled every other cause out and we guessed it must be some weird allergy no one had ever heard of. We were running out of ideas or medical diseases that could explain it. Then I remembered what the nurses said about the abnormal clotting after the milkshakes his wife had brought in.

After the latest blood transfusion and the return of his blood prothrombin to normal, I started digging through his trash. I had spoken to the chief of pathology and told him of my suspicions. I walked a used milk shake container to his office the next morning and he took it right away to test it in his research lab. He had a fancy gizmo that could tell what even a mosquito had for breakfast.

I got the answer the next day.

The team leader and I sat down with "the bleeding guy" and told him what the chief of pathology had found on the milk shake container his wife had brought to him.

"I knew we were having some problems, but I had no idea how bad things could get!" he spoke to me in a quiet voice.

Mr. D'Antonio's blood tests returned to normal over the next several days.

It was my day off when we met in the patient's room with the police. Mr. D'Antonio was in his street clothes after we had given him discharge paperwork. He summed it up like this:

"My wife was trying to poison me and could have killed me if I hadn't come to Jackson.

These doctors and nurses saved my life, even as my wife was even coming to the hospital with the rat poison mixed into the milk shakes."

The case was unusual, even for Miami, Florida. The newspaper gave it a big headline, "Local woman arrested for attempted murder of her husband by poisoning."

I didn't find out any more about what the nurses called the "D'Antonio case." Way too many other crimes and tragedies forced it off the front pages.

But I had learned the value of my mentor's advice: "Listen carefully to the patient, the diagnosis is always in the history." What I had also learned was that asking the right question always gives the correct answer to the patient's problem.

It would take a life time in Emergency Medicine to teach myself how best to ask that right question of patients. When I found myself stumped in patient care, the answer was always found in a telling detail, if only I had the patience to ask and, more important, to listen.

Chapter 7
Hampton VA Hospital

"This guy's feet are about to fall off. This is the worst case of trench foot I've ever seen."

I was working a few weeks at the Hampton Veterans Affairs (VA) Hospital prior to my military service and the M.O.D. (M.D. on Duty) in the ER wanted me downstairs. I trotted on down and saw "trench foot." I turned the corner and saw a familiar face. His name was Bill Green and I had treated his chronic immersion skin disease at the Miami VA Hospital just four months ago.

"Hi Bill," I called out. "Are you still using the potassium permanganate solution I prescribed for your feet?"

He did a double take when he recognized me, picked up his things and walked out of the hospital without saying anything. Maybe it was my look of amusement that did it.

The M.O.D. swiveled between looking at me and at Bill's back as he walked out of the hospital.

"Another cure for the team," he commented wryly. "Nice work!"

One of the more experienced nurses told me about the "vacation circuit." That's where the patient games the system at multiple VA hospitals, essentially getting free room and board, treated and improved at one hospital, then neglecting their meds, making things worse to get admission at the next. I had seen this in Bill Green's behavior, his purposeful self-neglect to get the secondary gain of a free vacation home. The Bill Greens knew that they could call their Congressman and make trouble for the local VA hospital if they were not given what they demanded. It was a bad system, and clearly headed for disaster and public condemnation in the future.

The M.O.D. in the VA hospital ER had a mandate to admit all the patients who demanded admission, regardless of the medical condition, so his latest page to me sounded like another Bill Green case.

"I got a guy says he's got diarrhea," the M.O.D announced over the phone. "Come down and admit him."

He had admitted many patients to the Internal Medicine service. So far, every patient had been a "social admission." I thought these patients should have been cared for in the outpatient service, not taking up a hospital bed. It was clear, I was too dumb to get it. This was the Government and many of the patients were demanding. The complaints of the patients go straight to Congress. A Congressional Inquiry must, by law, be answered, in writing by the Hospital Administration within three days. So, to keep the peace, the VA required the M.O.D. to admit patients that other hospitals would not. To keep the job is to not buck the system. That's a lesson I was too young to comprehend.

The patient was a young soldier, Fred Kean, he was twenty-five years old, close to my age, so we could talk as equals. He was honorably discharged and told me that he was no longer eligible for care in a military hospital. He was instructed to go to the VA hospital for any further treatment.

"I was in-country for eighteen months," he said. "I ran a grader as part of my job in an engineering battalion. The unit maintained the runways at a small Army airfield."

His complaint was continuous diarrhea since returning from Vietnam, about six months ago. He had been treated at the Army dispensary at the base and it helped for a while.

"Everybody had the shits over there. The food was O.K., but the stress and the heat made everybody drink a lot of water. The Army medical officer helped get us bottled water most times, but it wasn't enough. Most of us went downtown to drink in the dinky bars. The beers went down good after a hot day on the grader or pouring tar."

He had grown up in Virginia and had some family in the Roanoke area. He had always been a hunter and fisherman and spun some funny yarns about camping in the woods, running away from a black bear that wanted the fish he had hooked.

But the reason he was here was serious. His chart showed that he had lost forty pounds in the last year. He was initially treated in the U.S. Army hospital in Japan with no diagnosis. They shipped him to Letterman Army Hospital in San Francisco where he stayed for two weeks, again with no diagnosis. The chart was full of normal lab tests and consults with gastroenterology specialists. They were all stumped. He got transferred to Walter Reed Medical Center in Washington, D.C., so he could be closer to home. The Walter Reed doctors concluded that his belly pain and diarrhea were psychosomatic, all in his head. They prescribed Valium, which made him sleepy, but didn't stop the diarrhea. He was discouraged.

"Doc, I been through the Army mill and they don't know why I still got the shits."

I told him that I would start him on IV fluids to keep him hydrated, and only allow a clear fluid diet. He knew this drill and agreed to it.

The Army psychiatrist's note was vague, not really explaining the situation. I could imagine that eighteen months in a combat zone, followed by the distress of undiagnosed and untreated diarrhea, would cause anxiety and fears. He opined that the soldier was having a "delayed stress reaction," which was descriptive, but not useful to me in treating the patient. He recommended consideration for involuntary separation from the service. This sounded to me that, basically, they were going to throw this guy out because he couldn't be diagnosed and cured. Kicking a young man out of the service with a psychiatric diagnosis could have major social and financial consequences for his entire life. I was going to do my best to find out what was really causing his diarrhea. I couldn't believe that stress was the cause, and not the consequence.

I spent most of my free time the next week studying his medical record, all eight hundred pages of it. He had had an extensive tropical medicine work-up at Letterman with no findings. Walter Reed had done a repeat of that and did extensive bowel x-rays and even a biopsy of his liver, all tests, again normal. All the blood, urine, and stool cultures were noted as normal.

One blood test showed a slight anemia, his hemoglobin was 12.5 grams. Normal adult males range from thirteen to fifteen grams. Not a big deal and certainly not diagnostic. In my limited, rookie knowledge of things, it didn't seem to me that psychologic distress by itself could cause anemia.

I examined each of my patients every morning around breakfast time. This young man had to go to the john after eating the Jell-O and tea in his clear fluid diet. I asked him through the closed bathroom door if he could give me a stool sample. I took the fresh specimen to the lab and went back upstairs to my ward.

I repeated this for the next three days. Fresh stool sample handed to me from the bathroom; I run it down to the lab and then back upstairs to the ward to see my other patients.

At the nurse's station, they handed me the phone. It was the head tech in the lab and he was exasperated. "Why do you keep bringing us stool samples every day?" he asked. "Your patient is passing Giardia, big time!"

The nurses could hear the loud angry voice on the other end of the line and they were curious to see me grinning ear to ear. Finally, a real, treatable diagnosis!

Giardia lamblia is an intestinal parasite that attaches to the wall of the intestines and robs the patient of nutrients, but it does not kill its host. When it reproduces, it drops its eggs into the stool stream. To see it under the microscope you must have a fresh stool specimen and experienced eyes to see the telltale eggs.

Most patients get Giardia by drinking contaminated water. Beavers and other wildlife seem to be carriers and release the microscopic eggs into water. I had no idea how he had caught this in Vietnam, but the beers in the local bars sounded suspicious to me.

The head lab tech was from the Caribbean and had seen plenty of parasites. He knew what to look for and was only too happy to show me the eggs under the microscope. They were weird little cross-eyed swimmers. I remembered seeing them in my two weeks studying Parasitology in Med School.

I started proper treatment with oral Flagyl pills. Within a week of taking the pills the diarrhea stopped. He began to gain weight. I continued taking fresh stool samples to the lab each morning until they were negative, and no more Giardia seen.

Fred and I talked a lot about his future, now that he had a future, untroubled by diarrhea.

"I am going home and work on my Dad's land," Fred told me. "You can bet that I won't be taking any water out of the streams!"

We laughed. He turned to me and asked a serious question: "How come you, a new doctor, could cure me and all those big-wigs at Walter Reed couldn't help me with all those fancy tests?"

I think that in the big hospitals his stool samples must have sat around, drying out and killing the parasite. Giardia need a moist environment to survive. It takes a lot of trouble to take fresh stool samples, daily, by hand, to the lab. But it is the best way to make the diagnosis. Fred didn't want all that science blather. He wanted a story to tell his family about the rookie doctor who helped him get well. So, I said with a smile, "Even a blind pig can find the acorn sometimes!"

We shook hands on that note and I walked him out the door of the VA hospital and watched his family drive him home.

This case taught me that experts can make mistakes, sometimes because they consider themselves infallible. If they can't find the answer, then the patient is 'blamed' and must be mental. It brought home that being a "blind pig," thinking about the patient as a person, not a number to be processed, can find the proper care, that "acorn."

When the ER is chaotically busy, it is essential to be a "blind pig," to be aware of one's thinking, and to try to be objective. It is a very difficult mindset to attain, when fatigued and stressed, but essential to excellent patient care. The ancient aphorism that "Luck favors the prepared mind," applies many times in taking care of hurt and scared patients. My early experiences in the ER taught me that remembering stories of success should be tempered with stories of failure, like the story of Fred Kean, whose diagnosis was missed again and again by highly competent military doctors in the best military centers we have. I learned to observe and treat patients by what I had seen, not be instructed by others. It is much easier to join the chorus than to try to sing solo. These remembrances formed the core of my early clinical skills, to be added to daily.

Chapter 8
USAF Tour of Duty

I had been an ROTC (Reserve Officer Training Corps) cadet in college and after completing my internship and passing my licensure examination to become a recognized physician, I was commissioned a captain in the United States Air Force (USAF). It was the culmination of nine years of intensive book learning capped off by clinical education on the wards of the University of Miami Medical School hospitals.

Now that I had a job and an income to support my family, I could start to pay off my education loans. My parents had supported us through some very lean times and I was glad to repay them the money from my first paycheck from the USAF.

By the end of four years of active duty, I completely paid off the loans that had helped pay for my education. I was grateful for the USAF job, making new friends and traveling to many countries, but the medical work was not challenging. Most of my patients were very fit young flying officers and their young healthy families. My responsibilities were to organize and supervise immunizations for world-wide military service. I also made sure the flight crews were healthy for flying. Since the flight crews were young and healthy people, there was not much real doctoring to do. I did volunteer to work some shifts in the base hospital ER, but it functioned as a night walk in clinic, not a true ER.

A colleague in the USAF tipped me to a moonlighting job at the local civilian hospital. I was not challenged by my day job, so I applied to the ER doctors there and they hired me.

It was a busy place and the Chief of the ER had the moonlighters work on the clinical side of the ER, no trauma, but lots of sick patients. I liked the variety of patients and enjoyed working with the experienced nurses. Over the months that I did this part-time work, the nurses taught me the fastest way to size up a patient and get appropriate treatment.

Most of these patients had simple needs which we could easily meet. Asthmatics needed some epinephrine shots and a bronchodilator nebulizer prescription. I treated lots of colds, flu, and urinary tract infections. Some nights it was STDs (sexually transmitted disease) and belly aches.

The nurses showed me how to get sensitive history from many patients too ashamed to tell "the Doctor." Most patients were not candid about three areas of their lives. It was always, "two beers," when asked about alcohol intake. Everybody would, on prodding, shyly admit to "reefer." But, no one, and I mean no one, wanted to tell me about their sexual contacts, especially when those contacts were extramarital or between the same sexes.

I could count on the nurse's eye rolls when hearing a fanciful response to my early questions in the three forbidden topics. Gradually, and with learning to hear the unsaid as well as the patient's words, I got better at it.

Not many of these walk-in patients needed to be admitted to the hospital. When they did require admission, I would call their physician and arrange for their care. I learned how each of these doctors wanted the initial hospital orders to be written for their patients. Some orders would be brief, and others would need to be detailed, depending on the medical issues.

As a moonlighter, I was not considered to be on the same professional footing as the private physicians who practiced full time at the hospital. Sometimes that was made clear to me by having my judgment questioned directly by the physician I consulted for on an admission.

Jervis Taylor was a "frequent flyer" in the ER. He had come to the hospital every month with complaints of "belly aches." He was an unemployed, forty-three-year-old man who drank every day. He did some day labor on occasion, but no steady job. Jervis liked the very cheapest stuff he could get, mostly malt liquor in "forties," and rotgut wine. He stayed out of trouble with the police and lived in the neighborhood behind the hospital. He walked and rode the bus, didn't have a car. He told me that his bicycle had been stolen last year and he didn't have the money to get another one.

I had examined him many times before and found his blood tests showed elevated liver enzymes and slight anemia, nothing unusual in an alcoholic. His rectal examination did not reveal any bleeding and I often prescribed antacids. I knew he wouldn't get a prescription filled so I dispensed samples from our small supply given to us by drug company representatives. These samples were locked up in the ER and were given to patients like Jervis who could not afford to buy them.

Jervis had his usual complaint of belly ache and admitted to the same alcohol intake. He had finished taking the sample antacids but felt worse. He looked acutely ill to me, with thinning of his face, especially temporal wasting. He had a sallow complexion with a yellow cast to his eyes of jaundice, which I had seen many times from his alcohol abuse. But the temporal wasting, hollowing of the facial temporal muscles, was a serious new physical finding. It means that the body has begun to destroy its muscles metabolically. I had seen it in patients suffering advanced cancers and in chronic debilitating diseases, but rarely in alcoholic patients. This meant that Jervis was dying from his chronic alcohol abuse.

On examination, Jervis had tenderness in the upper part of his stomach and some hemorrhoids, but no blood in the rectum. The lab tests were markedly abnormal now. The liver tests were higher than before and now pancreas tests were markedly elevated, too.

He did vomit some clear fluid in the ER. He told me that he couldn't keep his wine down and was worried he might get "those DT's again." Delirium Tremens is a dangerous syndrome of alcohol withdrawal with seizures and hallucinations, mental confusion, and disorientation. It has a mortality rate of five percent, but the risk of death is reduced in patients receiving adequate medication and medical support.

I started an IV with normal saline and glucose solution to which was added multivitamins. This bright yellow solution in a plastic bag, hanging from the IV stand is called a "Banana Bag," for obvious reasons. Banana Bags replenish the alcoholic's vitamins to prevent brain damage, expand the fluid volume to replace dehydration from vomiting, and the glucose solution gives vital fuel to the brain, as well as, the patient's muscles. I also started medicine to prevent seizures from developing as Jervis was unable to keep wine down.

Jervis had damaged his liver and now his pancreas was also affected. He could not digest food, and even clear liquids caused pain in the swollen pancreas. I had started treatment in the ER, but he would have to be admitted for continued treatment.

My experiences from the University of Miami and from my short stint at the VA Hospital made the admission of an alcoholic with pancreatitis to the hospital a certainty. I had never had push-back on admissions in those settings and, when the shoe was on the other foot, I always accepted the patient to my service without a quibble. That was just how it was done in my world, but I was now in a different world.

I looked up the service roster of attending physicians and found a name for internal medicine cases. It was about 8 PM on a Wednesday so I thought this would be a straightforward transaction. I call the doctor, explain the case, he accepts, and Jervis gets a hospital bed.

I called the internal medicine physician, Dr. M.T., at home, introduced myself and began to ask for his help.

"I'm not on call today!" And he slammed the telephone down in my ear.

I quickly reviewed the call list and even asked the attending ER physician in the trauma center next door if Dr. M.T. was, indeed on call.

"Yep, that piss ant is on call, don't let him give you any shit!" was his advice to me.

I called Dr. M.T. again and before he could say a word I told him that the attending ER doctor had confirmed that he was on call.

"O.K., what kind of crap are you dumping on me now?" he angrily replied.

I briefly told him the diagnosis I had arrived at for Jervis and the lab tests which supported it, then I paused to let him speak.

"So, what do you want me to do about it?"

"I want you to admit him for his pancreatitis," I said, trying to remain reasonable.

"Nah, that's a GI problem, call them." And he hung up the phone again.

I was baffled by this and more than a little bit angry. I turned to the nurse who had heard most of this and asked her, "Do we have a gastroenterologist on staff?"

"Yes, doctor, but he doesn't take ER call, he just sees patients in consultation," she said.

I found Dr. K's number and called him. He is Korean, and we had some difficulty understanding each other.

"I'm sorry, but I don't admit. I will be happy to consult in hospital. You should call the medical doctor. Thank you." He was extremely courteous, but unable to help me more.

It was now 9:30 PM, my shift ended at 11 PM, and I had other patients to see, so I was not going to take any more guff about admitting Jervis.

Usually as a courtesy to the physicians I admitted patients to,

I would write initial hospital orders, but I wasn't about to do that for Dr. M.T. tonight.

I called Dr. M.T. and told him about my conversation with the gastroenterologist.

"Okay, go ahead and write some orders, and I'll see him tomorrow," he said dismissively.

I responded in what I hoped was a professional way, trying not to let my anger bleed into the conversation too much, "I'm unable to do that for you since you hung up on me twice and treated me like a flunky. You'll need to come to the hospital now and see the patient yourself."

The phone was silent and then he said,

"I don't appreciate your rudeness, I'll be over there tonight," and he slammed the phone down again.

Dr. M.T. stormed into the ER and made a show of belittling Jervis about his drinking, and pointedly ignoring my presence. He grabbed the chart from the nurse and scribbled some orders, handed it to her, then turned and walked out of the emergency department.

The nurse showed me the orders and I saw that they were incomplete. There was no provision to treat the pain of pancreatitis and no intravenous fluid replacement that accompanied pancreatitis. I wrote the proper orders on the ER chart, not on the admission order sheet, to avoid the appearance of contradicting Dr. M.T.'s decisions.

I finished all my cases by 11 PM and walked over to the Trauma Center. I related the entire episode with Dr. M.T. to the attending ER doctor, who smiled and said, "You'll fit in here just fine. M.T. needed to get his butt in here for that patient tonight!"

Two days later, on my next shift, I called the ward upstairs to learn that Jervis had been discharged. He had been in the hospital less than a day, discharged the morning after by Dr. M.T., who recommended Jervis go to the ER for any further care. Dr. M.T.'s final chart noted that Jervis should not have been admitted at all, that he could have been treated as an outpatient.

I was flabbergasted. How could you treat an alcoholic patient with pancreatitis, a dangerous combination that could lead to dehydration and death, like that? That was not the way I had been trained, and I worried that the police would find Jervis dead in some alley. But that didn't happen.

Jervis did survive, as I saw him the following week, again drunk, and with belly pain. I was able to get him admitted at the local VA Hospital this time, since he had been a combat wounded Vietnam veteran, and they also had medical records on his conditions.

This was not the last time I would have to negotiate a patient's admission or outpatient follow up. I considered the ER a vital safety net for many people. I also considered it a moral obligation for physicians to try their best to serve those patients, no matter how undesirable they may seem to some. The patients like Jervis are with us always, suffering and being marginalized. They need help, not scorn.

Chapter 9
My Foolish Pride

After my Air Force tour of duty ended, I was hired by the ER doctors for whom I had moonlighted. I was untested, but very sure of myself, thinking I was ready for anything. I was going to work my first shift as a solo ER doctor in the busy Hampton General Trauma Center, and I was excited by the adrenaline rush.

"We have a casualty from the lumberyard," the paramedic radio call came in suddenly.

I tied the knots of the last sutures in a patient's hand wound and asked the nurse to apply a dressing, then I heard the diesel engine of Hampton EMS-1 just outside the sliding doors to the ambulance entrance.

It was a very hot, humid summer day, with the broken promise of rain. The sky was overcast with hazy clouds backed by a greasy sun. All of us on the ER team were feeling the miserable weather and hoping for a storm to blow the heat away.

The medics brought in a young man, barely breathing, and unresponsive to the nurse's questions. They had started an IV in the three-minute drive from the lumberyard to our back door. That commercial outfit supplies wood made into roof trusses, shipping them by barge to Baltimore.

They have had to pull the patient out from under the lumber loader. This machine is one hundred feet long and six feet wide, a moving powered belt which transfers finished boards down from the saws on the top floor to the assembly yard, where they then make up the roof trusses.

The foreman who called the Rescue Squad, told them this man had shut the power off, then crawled under the lumber loader to remove a jammed board. Another worker, not seeing him under the loader, restarted it, stopping when he heard the screams.

The paramedics gave me this history as they transferred him to the ER stretcher. The patient was covered in sawdust clinging to his sweaty face, chest, and back. His head lolled back as they moved him, and he was gasping for air. I felt a very faint pulse at his wrist and his eyes were closed.

I helped cut away his work shirt, brushing sawdust off. I put my stethoscope to his chest and heard muffled heart sounds with shallow breathing. There were deep bruises on the right side of his chest and ribcage. I knew that this meant the clock was running on "The Golden Hour," the time immediately after traumatic injury when the highest likelihood of our ER care to prevent death exists. Any delay greatly reduces the chance to save the trauma patient's life.

I searched for injuries as we took off the dirty boots, socks, and canvas work pants. His limbs looked straight and I didn't see or feel swelling of his belly. I ran my hands all over his head and along the spine, nothing was out of line or swollen. I shined my penlight into his eyes to check his pupils, looking for inequality or sluggishness, which could indicate a brain bleeding. His pupils should constrict instantly with the bright light, but they were slow to react. I worried that his brain was not getting enough oxygen or glucose. This was the onset of coma, and I better do something quick about it. He would stop breathing in minutes without my intervention.

A small part of me considered the possibility of drug or alcohol causing this, but without any conscious thought I had rejected that. He had the smell of a worker outside in the heat, no alcohol, but sweat and sawdust filled my nostrils. This is pattern recognition that all experienced ER docs do, an instinctual limiting of the myriad possibilities in a trauma patient.

I opened his mouth and inserted the lighted laryngoscope, which looks like a six-inch bent spoon with a long handle on the end. I gripped that handle with my left hand, advancing the smooth blade over the tongue, careful not to use his teeth and jaw as a lever. Tongue, mouth, throat had no blood or puke as I kept lowering the light. I inserted the endotracheal tube through his epiglottis, a valve-like thumb that keeps our swallowed food and drink going to the stomach and not into the lungs. I injected some saline into the injection port, a small tube that runs down the side of the endotracheal tube ending with a cylindrical balloon. This small amount of saline inflates the balloon, seals the passage, and prevents anything from the mouth getting in his lungs. His lips were still blue and his breathing was slowing down.

The ER team had sent blood to the lab and the nurses had passed a Foley catheter into the patient's bladder. The amount of urine being produced is an indicator of the patient's circulation status. When the urine flow stops, the trauma patient is entering a shock state. Low blood pressure, scanty urine formation, and sluggish pupil reactions to bright light are all dire signs, which if not corrected lead to circulatory failure and death.

He had stopped breathing. He was near death, and I squeezed

the Ambu bag to deliver oxygen into his lungs, breathing for him. His color was improving with each puff and I was continuously examining him as the treatment continued. I learned early in my career that, in trauma, there are simultaneous life threats that must be dealt with for the patient to survive. The "ABC'S"- airway, breathing, and circulation, form a mantra that was right at the top of my thinking. I was asking myself, "Is the airway secure?" I saw that the endotracheal tube was not bitten, bent, or pulled out of place. Check. Next, I watched the breathing, which I did for the patient with my Ambu bag. "Do both sides of the chest wall inflate equally with each puff I gave?" I saw that his "circulation," indicated by the pulse rate and blood pressure, was abnormal. The low blood pressure and high pulse rate told me that the patient was bleeding internally, since there were no external wounds seen. Intravenous saline was running into both arms and his blood had been sent to the hematology lab for cross-match. I knew he would need blood transfusions to survive in the ER.

Immediately, I saw that the right side of his chest did not rise and fall with each puff. That meant that something was blocking the air flow into the right lung. In trauma, it might be a collapsed lung or worse, bleeding in the lung. One other possible cause is that the endotracheal tube had slipped, giving air to one side only. The endotracheal tube has ruled measuring marks on the side and I knew that the proper depth from the teeth to the tracheal carina, the "Y" junction that divides the airway into left and right, is twenty-two centimeters. I saw the marking "22 cm," and knew it was in the proper place.

I was at the patient's head, pumping oxygen into him with the Ambu bag. I had to squeeze the bag with more force to make his chest wall rise, a sign that he was getting worse and would suffocate if I didn't act soon. I looked again at the right side of his chest not moving and call for the emergency chest tray. There was no time for chest x –rays to find the cause. If I don't relieve the blockage in his right lung now, he'll die.

I gave the Ambu bag to a nurse, put on sterile gloves and opened the sterile chest tray set up on the Mayo stand next to the patient's right side. I had never used a chest trocar before and I picked it up to examine it. The trocar looks like a medieval torture device. It is stainless steel, eighteen inches long with a sharpened two-inch long point. It is hollow so a flexible, plastic chest drainage tube can be threaded through it quickly. It had been created for just this emergency where seconds count. Normally, I would take several minutes to carefully insert a chest tube to drain fluid from the lung, time which, I judged, this patient didn't have.

The nurse gloved up and poured Betadine all over the patient's chest, splashing the brown antiseptic all over the stretcher and onto the floor. I was nervous and felt my left hand slipping on the wet skin as I lined up chest wall landmarks to guide me. If I'm too low, I'll spear his liver and kill him. If I'm too high, I may put a hole in his lung and kill him. I felt the sweat drip off my forehead onto my nose. I put my anxiety aside-it was do or die time.

I didn't hesitate as I shoved the trocar into the patient's chest with a hard push. I felt the grinding as I rammed the sharp point through chest skin, muscle and rib cartilage into the pleural space lining the lung. Immediately, there was a rush of dark blood splashing onto the floor. The nurse working the Ambu bag shouted that she could move air into the patient better, but his blood pressure had dropped. I heard the heart monitor screaming in alarm-his heart rate was rocketing.

I passed the plastic chest tube through the trocar and pulled the vicious looking instrument out of him. I clamped the chest tube with a large hemostat to prevent air from sucking back into his chest, while I secured it, taking big bites with thick silk suture and tying it down. The bottom end of the chest tube got pushed into a collector, with a water seal, a valve that allows trapped air and blood out of the lung, but not back into the patient.

The ER team had begun two blood transfusions as I was securing the chest tube. Many skilled hands, working together in this crisis have given this young man a chance to survive his injuries. Our ER unit secretary was an important part of the team and had gotten the on-call surgeon and the OR team alerted. She had mobilized thirty doctors, nurses, and OR technicians to save him.

The OR nurse and technician rushed to the patient's bedside, taking a hurried report from the ER nurse. I snapped off my bloody gloves and helped push the stretcher through the open elevator doors. I squeezed the Ambu bag and saw that the foamy blood was not spurting through the chest tube into the collector strapped to the stretcher frame, a sign that his lung had expanded. The elevator doors opened to the air-conditioned surgical suite and I handed my patient off to the anesthesiologist and the surgeon. As the OR door swung shut, the sweat on my face and armpits dried, giving me a chill. My heart began to slow to normal as the nurse and I rode the elevator down to the ER, both of us saying silent prayers for the patient's survival.

I spoke to the surgeon a few hours later. He told our ER team that the patient had a crushed spleen that was pouring out blood into his abdomen. The patient's liver was split and the surgeon packed it with Gel Foam to stop the hemorrhaging. He complimented the ER:

"He had severe crush injuries and it's a miracle that you were able to resuscitate him."

This surgeon had just finished several hours in the OR, giving eight units of blood, clotting factor transfusions, and normal saline before stabilizing the patient's blood pressure and pulse rate.

A very heroic surgeon, who flat out, would not give up. The anesthesiologist, who also never stopped working, was still with the patient in the surgical recovery unit, as were the OR nurses and technicians.

Over the next two weeks I would go up to the Intensive Care Unit after my shift to check on the patient. I would share the news with the rest of the ER team. He was in the ICU for another week then transferred to the Intermediary, Step-Down Unit, which despite the name, was really a promotion. The Unit nurses said he was improving a lot.

That good news gave us all a needed boost after stressful ER shifts over the weeks. I visited him in the Step-Down. He was bandaged up and the chest tube had been removed. He still had a saline IV dripping, but he was sitting up and eating a hospital meal. He, of course, didn't recognize me. I introduced myself to his father and to him, putting out my hand to the patient. He was sullen, eyes downcast, and silent. He didn't want to talk to me and refused to shake my hand. He certainly was not interested in my crowing about how the ER and I had saved his life.

His father stood up and thanked me and the ER team for saving his son's life. He was very gracious to me. I apologized for the interruption and left them alone, muttering something about going to work downstairs. I later reflected that I must have interrupted a serious father-son conversation and felt embarrassed for my thoughtless intrusion. I also felt silly at my intention to brag about our ER care. I knew we had done a wonderful job in saving his life. After all, didn't the surgeon praise me and the team as miracle workers?

It was a bitter lesson, didn't I deserve gratitude, even praise? What I learned then and often, was that my pride meant nothing to the suffering patient. As I thought more about my lack of humility, I was deeply ashamed of myself. I chose this profession to help others, not to aggrandize myself, no matter how marvelous I performed. Pride is much different from self-confidence. I had a lot of growing up to do.

Three months from the day he was injured, the patient developed liver failure and lapsed into a coma. He had been transferred from our hospital to Medical College of Virginia, the large teaching center in Richmond, Virginia. Despite the paramedics, the ER team, the heroic surgeon, all the ICU nursing staff, and the excellent, expert care at one of the best University Medical Centers, our twenty-two-year old patient died.

In some way, it felt to me that he had died twice. Once when the lumber loader crushed him and the ER saved him, and now at MCV. I felt terrible at his death, as did all the other members of the ER team. With this bad news, many in the ER wept.

One of the ER nurses on the team the day when the patient was brought in attended the same church as the patient's family. She learned that the day of the injury had been his first day on the job. A job his father insisted he take.

Chapter 10

MVA (Motor Vehicle Accident)

It had been raining steadily, making the roads slick. At 7 PM, Friday, I walked into the ER to start the night shift, expecting to be busy. I hung up my raincoat and got a report from the dayshift doctor. Usually there are a few patients, whose evaluation and treatment spans the change of shift, some are awaiting hospital beds, finishing treatment, or waiting on lab tests. I had learned to re-examine these holdover patients whose diagnosis is unclear. It can be a burden to have five or six patients from the previous shift as your immediate concern, since new patients that you must see are pouring in the door, too. But mistakes are going to happen when corners are cut to speed care. Every emergency department and every ER doc has made those errors. The medical slang for these errors is "pitfalls." I guess the thought is to watch out for the quick, familiar decisions that seem correct, but are really a trap for the doctor and patient. The theory is easy but putting it into practice is hard. I was concentrating on one of the lab tests I had received for one of the dayshift patients when the alarm claxon sounded, signaling the paramedics are on the radio.

I picked up the telephone receiver and the medic told me:

MVA (Motor Vehicle Accident)

"We got a single truck accident. One patient. ETA five minutes."

Friday nights are the worst nights to be driving. My police friends tell me that half the drivers are drunk, high, or both. Add rain and wet roads and the stage is set for MVAs, motor vehicle accidents. I finished my review of the lab tests and felt confident that the diagnosis was correct and the patient could be sent home for outpatient follow-up. I wrote the discharge orders and left the chart on the desk for the unit secretary to handle.

The medics rolled the patient in "fully packaged' for safe transport to the ER. He was a young man on a backboard with a hard neck collar secured to the board to prevent any head or neck movements that could injure his spinal cord. He was also immobilized with a Velcro Spider. The Spider is a cleverly designed series of Velcro straps on a soft frame that attaches to the protective backboard. The upper straps keep the arms and chest secured from injury that movement might cause, yet give enough so the patient can breathe easily. The lower Velcro straps secure the patient's lower limbs, preventing harm. He was soaked, and water dripped off him to the floor.

I smelled alcohol on his breath. He was awake and mumbled when I spoke to him. I helped the medics do the three-man lift of the patient strapped to the board from the EMS transport stretcher onto the ER stretcher. I introduced myself and told the patient that he was in the ER. I still couldn't make out what he was saying. One of the nurses helping thought it sounded like a name to her, but it sounded garbled to me.

The paramedics yellow raincoats dripped water all over the floor as they helped the nurses roll the ER stretcher into the trauma bay. The trauma bay is large enough for two stretchers and two surgical Mayo stands, with all the resuscitation gear needed for major trauma care. Large overhead surgical spotlights are above the stretcher to fully examine the injured patient. Rolling IV stands allow fluids and, if necessary, emergency blood transfusions to be administered without blocking resuscitation staff. The trauma bay has two large pillars at the head of each stretcher. These pillars house the electrical outlets, oxygen lines, suction lines, and wires for the modular cardiac monitors which can be detached for each patient, as needed. The power pillars get all wires and lines off the floor, to prevent staff from tripping and falling.

The medics gave the history to me:

"Doc, his pick-up left the road and bent around a big tree. He was seat-belted with both airbags out. The windshield was starred, where he smacked it with his head, but there was no blood that we could see, but it's a frog choker out there. Hard to see anything on the road with all the rain blowing sideways. Some neighbor nearby heard the loud crash and called 911."

I helped the nurses towel off the water and examined the patient by removing the Velcro straps to see and feel his arms and legs. He moved them, and I didn't find wounds or bent bones. The nurses slipped off his boots and wet socks so I could examine his feet and ankles. I felt normal pulses in his feet and ankles, indicating to me that he did not have major arterial injury in his legs.

The nurses and I lifted his hips to pull off the wet jeans and shorts, while I rocked his hips and pelvis to and fro to test for stability. Long bone and pelvic fractures are painful, unstable, and can cause hemorrhage and circulatory collapse, if not treated in time. Usually, the injured patient will have signs of that severe trauma, but the brain injured or intoxicated patient may not cry out in pain when the fracture is moved by the staff.

I felt his belly and rib cage, finding no masses or broken ribs. I listened to his belly, lungs, and heart. His blood pressure and pulse were normal, and the cardiac monitor showed normal regular heartbeats, all signs of cardiovascular stability.

I loosened the Velcro Spider straps and felt his head and neck, running my hand down his entire spine. Palpation of his spine might reveal swelling or deformity of a fractured vertebra, indicating the real possibility of spinal cord injury, but I did not find any injury with my fingers. The nurses helped me cut off his wet shirt and then wrapped him in warm blankets to prevent hypothermia from the wet clothes and the room temperature IV's the paramedics had started in the field.

I ordered portable x-rays to be done in the trauma bay, not wanting to move him out of my sight. Trauma patients can become unstable with internal bleeding that may start without warning, so close observation is warranted.

I was called to attend another patient with a bleeding laceration from a knife fight, so it was about thirty minutes before I could return to the trauma bay. The x-rays were stuck up on the view boxes and I did not see broken bones. I was about to turn to see another patient when the nurse called me over to see him again.

He was now sobering up and asked me, "Where's Jenny at?"

The nurses and I were baffled. His speech had become clearer and he shifted around on the stretcher looking from the nurse to me.

I called the paramedics on the radio.

"Unit one, this is base, over."

"Base, unit one, over."

I instructed them, "Go back to the truck accident scene and search for another victim."

Thirty minutes later the medics came back to the ER with a young woman, soaking wet, packaged on the stretcher.

Jenny had taken off her seat belt just before her boyfriend had driven off the road into the big tree. She was ejected through the truck's sunroof, landing up in the branches of that tree. She was caught on a lower branch, unable to get down.

She was heavily intoxicated. I completed a full trauma examination and the x-rays showed both of her wrists fractured. I splinted both wrists and put both arms in slings. The nurses got the phone number of Jenny's parents and I called them at home at 2 AM. I asked them to come to the ER to take Jenny home. Jenny's father quickly told me that he would take the boyfriend home also. It was around 4 AM when they drove off.

MVA (Motor Vehicle Accident)

I was suturing another "fighter," so I missed what must have been an interesting conversation between Jenny's parents and her boyfriend.

Nurses to this day, joke among themselves, shaking their heads, "Where's Jenny?" I was not the only one who wondered why the truck's sunroof was left open in a rainstorm. The paramedics concluded that the driver was so hammered that he forgot to close it. I guess that made sense, but I knew it was a Higher Power that had opened the escape hatch. Jenny landed in the wet tree branches and only broke her arms. She didn't go through the sharp glass of the shattered windshield or break her neck like so may others had in similar motor vehicle accidents. It had to be a miracle.

Chapter 11
Cancer

"You have cancer!" is among the most frightening words a physician says to a patient. Many patients freeze up when they hear that diagnosis. They may think that the doctor was mistaken, talking to the wrong person. Okay, maybe the doctor was talking to me, but the diagnosis was incorrect, a mix up in the tests. It can't be true, this doctor is a quack, they think. Anything, but the dreaded truth, which may sink in or in some cases, continue to be denied.

The newer treatments are making cancer patients better, sometimes curing the cancer, too. The diagnosis of cancer is no longer the death sentence it once was.

When I was a boy one of my little league teammates died from leukemia. It was a big, scary word to my thirteen-year-old self that caused dread. I was one of Jimmy's pallbearers. He had been my friend, playing first base while I played third in the spring and early summer and now I was carrying his body to the church in the fall. As a teenager who thought he was immortal, Jimmy's death shattered that illusion for me forever. I knew cancer could kill, even a healthy, athletic kid.

Many years later our son had a little league baseball teammate with leukemia. Mark was about the same age as my friend Jimmy, but Mark had been treated at the Children's Hospital with chemotherapy and was cured. There would be no funeral for Mark. His life would go on from little league baseball to college. Mark fell in love, got married and had children of his own.

Still there are all too many who are not so fortunate. Nurse Allison called me from the nurse's station and lead me to room eleven. Room eleven is a large space with a positive pressure system. The air in the room is forced out by increased air pressure, preventing any air and germs from entering. It is the room we put patients with compromised immunity into to prevent hospital acquired infections.

I went to the sink, put on the paper mask, did a surgical scrub and gloved up. Allison also prepared before we opened the door.

We introduced ourselves to the patient and her mother who had brought her to the ER on the advice of the oncologist. She told me that the patient had been living alone, but now has moved in with the mother. As the patient began to speak, she was quickly interrupted by the mother, who monopolizes the conversation.

The patient is bald, very thin and weak, but she is scrappy and maintains some sense of humor when she said, "I feel crappy. This cancer is a real bummer!"

Mother interrupted the daughter to inform us that she had just finished the last of several rounds of chemotherapy and her blood count showed all the blood cells have been killed off.

This is a well-known and dangerous side effect of the treatment. The patient's body is now defenseless, with no germ fighting white blood cells. She is vulnerable to bacterial, fungal, and viral infections that can be rapidly lethal.

She had an elevated temperature of 102 degrees and some streaks seen on the portable chest x-ray taken in her room, indicating lung infection. Her urine was also full of bacteria when looked at under the lab microscope. And as expected, she was very anemic with only a few white blood cells to fight all these pathogens.

Allison and I started intravenous antibiotics and planned for ICU admission. I called the oncologist who was not hopeful. "Sharon has a very aggressive breast cancer and I think this is the end."

Several days later Allison called the ICU nurses and learned that the patient had not responded to any of the medicines and had died. Allison and I were working the same shifts over the next month and spoke about Sharon and her mother. Allison said to me, "I can't think of anything worse than a mother losing her child like that, even an adult child. Cancer can be so cruel."

I nodded in agreement, remembering other mothers and their children, as we went to see other patients together. I was surprised to see a man I knew pacing in the hall outside room nine.

"Hey Doc, please see my wife!"

Bill was the barber who cut my hair, always a talker, but not tonight. His face was drawn, and he was worried about his wife. Allison and I went into the room with Bill and made introductions. Joanie, his wife, tried to smile, but it is clearly an effort at politeness.

Joanie told us, "I have a really terrible headache and nausea all day. I can't eat and can't sleep."

She was normal in appearance with perfectly normal vital signs. Her medical history was unremarkable: a broken ankle, normal childbirths, and hysterectomy for uterine fibroids. She told us she was not taking medicines, doesn't smoke, use drugs or drink to excess. Furthermore, the headaches are, "All over my head, much worse if I cough or bend forward. I had migraines as a young woman, but this is much, much worse pain!"

I asked Allison to start an IV to administer medicine for the pain and nausea. I sent Joanie for a head C.T. I had foreboding about her headaches. I didn't like the severity of the headache or the symptoms making it worse with cough or bending over, both of which raise the spinal fluid pressure. Spinal fluid is a clear liquid that bathes the brain and its coverings, the meninges. If infection sets up in the spinal fluid it causes meningitis, which can cause headaches. Patient's with meningitis may have a fever with bacterial infection, Joanie's temperature was normal, however. Viral infections of the meninges may not have a fever associated, and I was hoping that might be the diagnosis, but as bad as that can be, it's treatable. In the back of my mind was the thought of a brain tumor causing increased pressure and Joanie's headache. I was counting on the head C.T. to find an answer.

Joanie was feeling better when she was wheeled back from Radiology. Allison smiled at her and helped her back onto the ER stretcher. The head C.T. results were called to me and I sat down on the chair next to the bed. The radiologist was certain. The C.T. shows cancer growing all through her brain. I told Joanie and Bill this terrible news. They were shocked and reeling, stunned into silent staring at each other and at me.

I had trouble dealing with this, too, but I had to swing into action. I asked Allison to immediately start intravenous powerful steroids, used by neurosurgeons and oncologists to reduce brain swelling from brain cancer.

At 3 AM I called the oncologist, apologized for the hour, and asked for an emergency appointment. He agreed and would see Joanie in his office at 9 AM, just six hours from now.

Several weeks later I received a report from the oncologist. Joanie underwent multiple radiation treatments to the brain metastases. A biopsy had been taken and a primary breast cancer had been discovered which responded to chemotherapy, since she was past the time when surgery could offer her help. The report concluded with a general plan and the note that the headaches were gone.

All of us deny the possibility of our deaths, it's a potent mental defense against the deeply felt certainty of the brevity of our lives. ER doctors and nurses have that very human trait, too. The difference is we try to ignore our fears and press on with our mission to cure if it is possible, to comfort always. One way we deal with the stress is humor, always ironic and black.

Practicing ER doctors and ER nurses must cover the emergency center day and night. The mock ad the nurses have posted on their desk, behind the counter so it is hidden from patients and visitors reads like this:

"ER CARE HOURS: 24-7-365! FAST -EFFICIENT- CHEAP PLEASE PICK ONLY ANY TWO."

I had started a string of dayshifts after several stressful nights, including that diagnosis of brain tumor masquerading as a severe headache at 2 AM. I felt better about Joanie, knowing that she was getting the best care. The nurses were relaxed and sharing stories about their children's antics with one another. It was shaping up to be a pleasant shift for us.

Allison had also rotated onto the dayshift and went with me to see a patient whose complaint was bellyache. I had a sinking feeling when I entered the patient's room.

After introductions, Mrs. Brown told us that her twenty-nine-year old husband had a bellyache today and was not eating. Allison and I looked at each other, silently asking why was his wife the informant? Competent adult patients who were seeking care, expressed that in the form of a health complaint, so what did this mean?

One of the other nurses on the ER team had been looking after the couple's two toddlers while Mrs. Brown gave us the history of the present illness, "Art has been sick only a few days with bellyaches, otherwise he's been fine."

Art Brown was gaunt with sunken cheeks. The muscles over his temples were atrophied. A sure sign of chronic wasting diseases, like AIDS, chronic tuberculosis, cancer, severe systemic arthritis like Lupus, and intestinal malabsorption. Mrs. Brown couldn't or wouldn't see the seriousness of Art's condition. Allison and I knew there was denial so profound as to make Mrs. Brown's account doubtful.

Art told me and Allison that, "Nancy doesn't believe in doctors, she thinks our faith will cure me and didn't want to come here. I've been sick for months, missing work, and throwing up every day. Today the vomit smelled like feces and she brought me here."

I examined Mr. Brown and found his belly was swollen and the bowel sounds were absent, a sign of a bowel blockage and a surgical emergency. I paged the surgeon on call and explained my findings. He examined the patient in the ER and got written informed consent for "exploratory laparotomy and treatment." Those terms meant that the surgeon would open him up and determine the best options for what was found in the belly.

The surgeon came down from the OR and told us the news.

"I opened him up and he was full of cancer. I did biopsies and diverted the bowel to form a colostomy. No possibility of surgical cure here."

The colostomy spares the patient a painful death from a ruptured colon. It only buys some time for the patient while the cancer keeps growing.

I found out later that Art Brown's tumor was a primary small bowel adenocarcinoma, a cancer that began in the bowel's mucus glands and then spread.

I had never heard of this cancer and found that the only treatment was an experimental chemotherapy at the National Institutes of Health. The estimated survival was only three months when the tumor blocked the intestines.

Many patients brought to the ER have exhausted their resources and have nowhere to turn. And some in permanent denial of their firmly diagnosed and treated cancer, seek a miraculous reversal of fate.

"He's back in room ten again," the triage nurse was not thrilled. She told me that the patient is a forty-two-year old man, an engineer by trade, accompanied by his devoted wife. They are childless, choosing to "travel the world," the wife had related to the nurse.

I reviewed the patient's medical record. He had been seen in the ER almost daily for the past two weeks and, reading between the lines, the nurses did not like this man, because of his demanding behavior. The record showed discharge referral to his oncologist and his primary care doctors after each ER visit. In the medical record was a quote from his oncologist. "We've done all we can for him. We have informed him and his wife, several times."

The record also detailed that the patient refused to accept this. He came to the ER daily wanting a different diagnosis, a more hopeful one. And, as much as we would love to have provided a miracle, we could not.

Allison has been his nurse on many occasions and wanted to help. We entered the patient's room and introduced ourselves. I sat by the bedside and asked all the same questions the patient had heard frequently.

Yes, he is eating. Yes, he is having formed bowel movements. Yes, he has adequate pain control. And finally, I asked him,

"Why are you here today?"

He responded with anguish, "I can't accept this diagnosis. I've been getting treatment for six months and I'm no better."

He looked at his wife. She had a wan smile on her face and after a second of eye contact, she looked away, clutching a balled tissue in her hand.

I knew the patient was a highly trained and experienced engineer, certainly he had had all his questions answered but one.

"Why me?"

I saw that he couldn't accept this emotionally, being in a state of angry denial. He is polite with me and the nurses, not abrupt or rude in answering our questions. He has not and will not accept the diagnosis of terminal cancer and what that means. His wife knew this and we saw the torment and anguish on her face.

Ultimately, I called one of his attending physicians who came to the ER and sat at the patient's bedside. Allison and I excused ourselves and left the room.

We walked over to the computer station and began entering

the required facts into the patient's medical record. After several minutes the patient's door opened and the patient, his wife and his attending physician walked out of the ER.

I mentioned that I didn't understand the patient's denial and repeated ER visits, almost daily. Allison typed her nurse's note into the patient's medical record and quietly said, almost under her breath, "I do. I understand him."

She looked over at me and pulled the top of her nurse's tunic to one side to show me a long surgical scar on her neck. I knew this scar, it has been made from a radical neck dissection operation for cancer.

Allison and I have worked together for months and this is the first time I had seen her scar. I had been impressed by her quiet kindness and compassion for our patients, especially for those suffering with malignancies. In the busy ER, the medical and nursing staff have little time to discuss our personal lives. A professional distance is comfortable for all.

She continued speaking, "I was only ten-years old when they discovered the lumps on my neck. It turned out to be cancer. I'm one of the lucky ones. Not all my friends on the cancer ward of the Children's Hospital lived. They gave me chemotherapy, but it made me real sick, throwing up and losing all my hair. My folks were great. I saw my mom cry only once on the wards. I begged them to make them stop giving me the 'sick medicine.' The doctors did stop the chemo and I'm glad to be cured." She paused to catch her breath and then continued.

"One of the oncology nurses helped me a lot. She held my hand when they stuck me and gave me the chemo. She knit a blue cap to put on my little bald head to keep warm. She read books to me and helped me coloring. I cried when I said goodbye to her when my parents took me home." Silence ensued.

"I've never forgotten her. That's why I went into nursing, to be like her when I grew up."

I wiped my eyes, held her hand, and spoke, "Allison, she'd be very proud of you. You have followed her example well, and the patients thank you for your kindness."

It's impossible for me to imagine the anxiety and tortures her parents must have endured during Allison's treatments. I know that the outcome was always in doubt, and the dread of finding a cancer recurrence never completely goes away for her and for her parents. Allison and other cancer survivors taught me that we all live day to day, with no promise of a tomorrow. That insight helped the little boy in me remember that shouldering my teammate Jimmy's little coffin into the church is not the inevitable end with cancer.

Chapter 12
The Knife and Gun Club

"We're bringing in a child who's been shot," the paramedic radio call heard over the noise of a busy Saturday night in the ER. The called meeting of the "Knife and Gun Club" had come to order. It was only 10 PM and I already had seen four people involved in a drunken brawl at a local nightspot. These customers had been sewn up, bandaged, and discharged. The ER was also busy with medical emergencies, too. I had started the work-up on a young man with severe bellyache, which could be appendicitis. All the ER rooms were full and seven other patients were there. One patient whose sexually transmitted disease had been treated with an antibiotic shot, is waiting the required twenty minutes to be certain he is not allergic to the medicine.

Freddie Jones was back with the agony of kidney stones again. The treatment was underway with intravenous pain and nausea medicines. He had had several x-rays which showed the pea-sized calcium spots of many kidney stones.

In another ER room, sixty-six-year old Mrs. Martha Elliot was being transfused. She had been brought to the ER by ambulance for vaginal hemorrhage. The paramedics were called by a neighbor who found her on the floor in a pool of blood. I had called in my friend Bob, the GYN on call, and he told me that it looked like the patient had a cervical cancer that had eroded into the ovarian artery. Mrs. Elliot was going to the OR immediately.

The room nearest to the ambulance bay doors was where

infectious patients were placed to reduce contaminating other patients and staff. The patient told the triage nurse, "I'm an alcoholic, had this cough for a month and cigarettes don't taste right."

She told me that she had come to the ER earlier, but, "The line to get in was too long, so I come back tonight."

Her name was Julie and she was homeless. The nurses knew her on sight, but I had never treated her. I was worried that her cough could be pneumonia, lung abscess, lung cancer or tuberculosis. There was no way to get the lab tests on a Saturday night and the very real possibility of Julie spreading tuberculosis reminded me of another personal risk faced by all who work in the ER. The risk of catching a fatal infectious disease from a patient. The nurses told me that Julie had signed out of the hospital last week when she had been admitted for alcohol withdrawal, the DT's or delirium tremens. She went out to start drinking again.

Another risk all ER workers face every day is violence. In the last year, a twenty-nine-year old ER doctor in a rural hospital had been shot to death. He was working a night shift attending a woman who had been beaten, when the woman's husband stormed into the ER shooting her and then the doctor. These thoughts were in my mind when I saw the ambulance bay doors open and the paramedics roll their stretcher in.

The patient was a little girl, maybe three of four years old. She had very wide-open eyes and seemed terrified by all the strangers around her. Several uniformed police officers were walking in with the paramedics. I recognized my friend Chuck, a police detective, who came up to me and the nurses. He related, "There were several gunshots fired in the street. We're still looking for the shooters. No help from the neighbors, who clammed up when the uniforms questioned them. This child was in her bed when bullets struck the house. So far, nobody will identify any of the shooters. Rescue on the scene heard mother's screams and investigated, found the child and the blood. Mother is coming to the ER."

I understood that the timid people in the neighborhood were rightfully afraid of becoming the next victim of the gangs. But, shooting a child in her bed? Where's the outrage? Where's the community disgust at this? I had seen too many examples of this violence in the same neighborhood, several streets near the hospital. The gangs intimidated everyone. I had to suppress these thoughts, or I would be too angry to function, so I pushed them down and got to work.

The little girl followed me only with her eyes, not moving her head. She was scared but not crying. Her little PJs had a cartoon character design and Bugs Bunny's smile was stained red. There was some dried blood in her hair, but I saw no active bleeding.

The child's blood pressure, pulse rate, and temperature were normal, but I noticed that she was not moving her right arm or right leg. It also looked like she had lost all feeling on her left side as the footed pajamas were slipped off, since she didn't move when I touched her left leg.

I began to get a sick feeling about these physical findings. The nurses had gently cleaned the dried blood and I saw a small round wound in the left side of the child's neck. She had been shot in the spine. The bullet had missed her carotid artery and jugular vein in her neck. If it had struck those blood vessels, the little girl would have bled to death. A bullet wound of the neck can also hit the top of the lung, causing collapse and hemorrhage, but her vital signs indicated to me that it had missed the lung.

X-rays of her chest and neck showed bullet fragments in one of the upper cervical vertebrae. The chest x-ray showed normal lungs and heart, but x-rays cannot show the damage done to her cervical spinal cord.

From the physical findings, I knew that the bullet had severed one side of her spinal cord, paralyzing the right side and destroying sensation on the left side of her body. This was a war wound, the Brown-Sequard syndrome, described in 1850 by a French surgeon. I learned the neuroanatomy well during my clerkships in neuro-ophthalmology and on the stroke service in medical school. The motor nerves cross over in the spinal cord in the neck, so the right arm and right leg motor fibers start out on the left side of the spinal cord, then down to the right-side muscles. The sensory fibers start in the spinal cord and do not cross, so the left side of the body is served by fibers coming down the left side of cord.

In this child, she had lost sensation of touch, vibration, position, pain, and temperature on her left side, since her sensory nerve fibers do not cross in the cervical cord. Her right leg and right arm were paralyzed, the motor fibers which cross in the cervical cord were damaged.

She was paralyzed on the right and insensate on the left.

I had not seen any parent yet, but I called the Neurosurgeon who took the child to the OR to remove the bullet fragments and broken pieces of her spine. In emergency care I am authorized to act in the place of parents to care for critically wounded or sick minor children. This law reasonably allows life-saving care to begin before parental permission can be obtained to start treatment.

The mother arrived in the ER at 3 AM and the nurses and I walked her to our small family room. We were seated, and I was still upset and had some trouble calming down as I listened to her.

"Her name Tanisha and I thought they done kilt her."

Tanisha's mom was young and wringing her hands as we sat together. She told me that the police told her Tanisha was brought to the ER and she had to get her sister to watch her other kids.

I told her that Tanisha had been operated on and was in the ICU and was expected to live.

"The bullet hit her in the neck and damaged her spinal cord, but I don't know how bad that will be for Tanisha."

The mother thanked us for saving her baby, and the nurses walked her up to the ICU.

I did hear months later from a friend who had a relative in Fishersville, Virginia, which is a center for rehabilitation spinal cord injuries. Tanisha was improving after treatment and would be coming home in a wheelchair.

My friend Chuck, who was now a homicide detective, told me that there were no suspects in the shooting of little Tanisha.

"Tanisha's mother and the other kids have moved to Fishersville to be near the rehab center. I intend to keep investigating. I'm hoping someone will give us a lead."

As I write this, many years later, no one had ever been charged for shooting Tanisha and ruining an innocent child's life.

Mrs. Elliot, the lady with the vaginal hemorrhage, did survive surgery and left the hospital.

————√\————

The young man with the bellyache did turn out to have appendicitis. He had it removed and went home two days later.

Julie had a serious bacterial pneumonia, spending three weeks in the hospital. She had a "stormy course," near death several times. She was put on a ventilator when she stopped breathing. She needed several antibiotics and treatment for the seizures caused by alcohol withdrawal. She finally recovered and was discharged to a half-way house. I asked the five medical specialists to share their treatment summaries and was not surprised to learn that she was lost to follow-up. Which meant that Julie didn't want anything to do with doctors or hospitals, ever again. She refused any further treatment.

Freddie Jones, the man with kidney colic pain, called the next day, complaining to the hospital administrator, "I'm not paying any of your bills! I couldn't rest, your damn ER is too noisy!"

Of course, I had to make a written reply to the hospital administrator's question about Mr. Jones's care in the ER. A written summary I had to compose on my day off.

Many such trivial complaints made the old saw true for me.

No good deed goes unpunished!

Chapter 13
Fast-Efficient-Cheap

I did smile when I saw the sign posted under the ER nurse's desk, then I thought that there was something that I did with patients that fits that bill. I touched and examined each one, every time I went into their rooms. Physical diagnosis was drilled into medical students in our sophomore year. I loved it because many times the answer was at the fingertips alone.

In the modern emergency and trauma centers of today the wonders of imaging by CT, MRI, PET scanning, nuclear isotopes, and ultrasound are vitally important to guide diagnosis and treatment. Patients and their physicians depend even more on these in office practice. But testing is sometimes slow and patients may have weeks of waiting to get certain imaging procedures. In addition, the testing can lead to even more imaging studies, not a very efficient use of the patient's time. And finally, these tests are run on very expensive machines and those who interpret the images are among the highest paid doctors.

I firmly believe in scientific, peer-reviewed studies of care and have used the latest technology to guide therapy, but these tests may not be definitive. The ER doctor must often use his or her senses as well as lab studies to help the patient. I made efficient diagnoses quickly and cheaply, using physical diagnosis that I learned years ago. I continued to search for physical findings to help care for patients, many times seeing patterns of illness and injury that would save lives.

Doug Rogers was a seventeen-year-old college freshman, home for summer break. Doug and his dad had been talking and laughing when it happened. He explained to me, "Dad told me a really good joke and cracked me up. I was chewing the cap of my BIC pen, laughing so hard tears were running out of my eyes."

He continued, "Then I noticed the pen cap was gone."

Doug and his dad looked between the sofa cushions and on the floor. They looked in his pockets and even inside his shirt. It was a mystery. Where was that plastic pen cap?

Doug told me that he was about to start his summer job as a lifeguard at the community pool, where he had worked each summer through high school. He had been on the high school swim team, and the coach got him the job.

He was worried about losing that job, since he had developed a cough today. Dad brought him to the ER to get cough syrup. Doug had coughed and coughed, getting red-faced and having some chest aches. He thought it might be the start of the flu, which would keep him off the lifeguard platform at the pool.

He was a tall, broad chested young man with the narrow hips of a competitive swimmer. His blood pressure, pulse rate, and oral temperature were normal. The nurse had put the pulse oximeter on his finger and the reading was 100%, perfect. The pulse oximeter fits over a fingertip, sending a fine laser light beam which penetrates the fingernail. The oxygen-rich red blood cells coursing through the microscopic capillaries under the nail bounce the laser beam back to the oximeter, which shows a number on the screen. The reading is based on the percent of red cells that are oxygen depleted. In Doug's case the oximeter confirmed that his lungs were working fine. There was plenty of oxygen in his red blood cells.

This was not flu or bad pneumonia. But what was it?

I put my stethoscope to the front of his chest and carefully listened to his heart. He had a regular heart beat and the normal sounds of heart valves opening and closing. There were no whooshing sounds of heart murmurs, or the tell-tale squeaking leather noise caused by an inflammation of the lining of the heart, pericarditis,

Next, I looked at his neck and saw normal pulses in the carotid arteries. I had him swallow as I felt the thyroid gland in the front of his neck. The thyroid was normal size and shape. Touching each side of his neck, I did not find any abnormal lymph nodes which might be associated with the constant coughing.

I listened to his chest with the stethoscope and heard distinct wheezing sounds on the left lung. The breath sounds of the right lung were normal. He coughed several times again as I was moving my stethoscope and I sent him for chest x-rays. When he was wheeled back from the radiology department, he jumped up on the stretcher and had several deep coughs that caused the stretcher to bounce up and down.

I listened to his chest and was surprised that the left lung was clear and now I heard wheezing in his right lung. I was confused.

What was wrong with me? Did I have a case of spatial dyslexia and couldn't tell left from right? Was this the beginning of a hearing problem or worse still, the earliest signs of dementia?

The chest x-rays were normal. Normal heart size. No sign of infection or mass in the lungs. Looking at these normal x-rays, the answer became clear to me. The Bic pen cap was made of plastic which, unlike metal pieces, was totally invisible to x-rays.

While laughing, Doug had aspirated; that is, breathed the Bic pen cap into his lungs. Furthermore, I knew where it had to be lodged and why it caused such deep non-stop coughing.

The pulmonary system starts at the nose and mouth, down the throat to the epiglottis, which is a fleshy, thumb-shaped check valve to prevent food from entering the lungs. In Doug's case, he took a deep breath after laughing so hard and the Bic pen cap whizzed by his epiglottis going toward his lungs. Below the epiglottis, the airway divides like a giant "Y" shape. One path of the "Y" goes to the right lung and the other to the left lung. The fancy medical name for this big "Y" is the carina. And I knew that the Bic pen cap must be at the carina. How else to explain wheezing in the left lung at one time and then the right lung later?

Now I had to convince the testy, reluctant thoracic surgeon of my diagnosis and get him to come to the hospital to remove the Bic pen cap from Doug's lung. Surgeons hate to be told what to do and this surgeon "knew" my diagnosis was wrong. He had a reputation for sounding off to the ER doc in front of patients and the nurses. He was technically a gifted surgeon, but desperately needed a charisma transplant.

I told him that my seventeen-year-old patient had an aspirated Bic pen cap at the carina. I pushed him over the edge, "You need to come in and bronchoscope him to remove it now."

I could feel the heat coming out of the phone in my hands as he shouted, "I doubt that, and you're probably wrong, as usual!"

After a short pause, to compose myself, I replied coolly, "Despite what you personally think about me, my patient has been steadily coughing for hours and has an aspirated foreign body. Please come in and help him."

The thoracic surgeon knows full well that once I have consulted him he shares medical liability for the patient just as I am obligated to note the time I have called him in the patient's medical record. His angry, insulting remarks never change that fact, and he knows it.

Two hours later the thoracic surgeon comes down from the OR where he had bronchoscoped Doug. He ambled over to the nurse's station where I had been writing orders on another patient. I looked up and he flips the Bic pen cap toward me.

I thought I saw a little bit of respect as he smiled, "You got it right, this time."

That was faint praise from this arrogant surgeon, but I'll take it. ER docs get a lot of push-back and vocal criticism from some surgeons who are perfectionists by nature. They are not sympathetic to the disorder and chaos in the ER. They demand every patient they see be fully worked up with all the tests neatly tied to the chart with a bow before they make their grand entrance.

Most patients have no idea of the arguments that happen between their doctors before they are admitted to the hospital from the ER. The patients would be dismayed to listen in to the ER doctor negotiating their specialist care, but it is a fact of life.

Doug was discharged from the recovery room before the end of my twelve-hour day shift. He and his dad made a point of coming by the ER, thanking the nurses and me.

Before the end of the summer, one of the nurses showed me a picture in the local newspaper. It was a picture of people at the side of the swimming pool. There was a mother and father holding the hand of a little kid alongside a tall young man in a red bathing suit, Doug. The caption simply read, "Life guard saves child at the community pool."

Chapter 14
Snow Day

Bad weather always means trouble is on its way to the ER, and the unpredicted snowfall brought many car accidents and falls our way. The radio call from the paramedics was different,

"We got two unconscious patients, IV's in place and oral airways, five minutes out."

The call got me remembering the other times I've dealt with several patients arriving simultaneously to the ER in serious condition. The anxiety and apprehension of confronting the unknown caused me to have the familiar sensations of racing heartbeat and sweaty palms. Scenarios and strategies came to mind immediately. My first thoughts were the treatment and disposition of current patients in the ER. Were any of these patients critical? Which patients were close to discharge from the ER? What lab tests and x-rays were being performed? I knew the arrival of two critical patients would need my full attention and help of many of the ER nurses. I explained to several of the patients and their families the reason for any delays. Most of the patients and families seemed to understand, but one patient was demanding and cursed at me. He was unconvinced that any other patient could be more important than his need for narcotics. I told him politely that I had no time to discuss it with him. He angrily walked out of this room, with the other patients staring at his back. The usual sounds of a busy ER were hushed as the angry man stomped out and slammed the door behind him. Relatives of patients who had been standing in the doorways of the rooms stopped chatting and a hushed silence fell over them.

The nurses and I had lots of experience in multi-tasking, keeping one eye on the patients on the ER stretchers, and one eye on the ambulance bay doors, waiting. We didn't have to wait long. The quiet was shattered as the sliding ambulance entrance doors opened with a loud bang, almost like a gunshot, and the medics rushed in with the first stretcher, tires squeaking on the polished floor.

The paramedics did chest compressions as they rolled over to the trauma bay. John Allen, the lead medic, shouted that the patient had arrested in the ambulance. The medics had been called to a downtown construction site by the work superintendent, who found the two men passed out.

The first patient, taking very shallow breaths and eyes closed, was not responding to the nurses. I looked at the resuscitation kit and Nurse Francis broke the seal and put it on the Mayo stand at the patient's head. Our emergency team didn't need words spoken in a crisis.

Out of the side of my eye I glanced over at the second room in the ER and saw one of the relatives standing in the hallway. She had wide eyes and her hand was covering her mouth, unable to avert her gaze from what must be a tableau in hell for her. Two big firemen pushing up and down on a man's chest, while the nurse and doctor seem to be onlookers, standing there.

I picked up the laryngoscope and endotracheal tube, opened the patient's mouth and smoothly passed the tube behind his tongue, down to the lungs. His tongue and the epiglottis, the small, thumb-shaped valve protecting his lungs from stomach contents, were limp. His tongue had fallen backwards and was partially blocking his airway. He was very close to suffocating to death. He stopped breathing and had only three minutes before the lack of oxygen caused heart and brain damage. There was no time to hesitate. I secured the endotracheal breathing tube to the Ambu bag and began squeezing air into him. I hoped I was in time to save him. Nurse Francis took the bag from me and continued squeezing. We stuck on the EKG leads, and the cardiac monitor over the top of the stretcher showed a normal heartbeat, for which I was grateful. I had intubated him just in time to avoid heart damage when he had stopped breathing.

The paramedics rolled in the second patient quickly. He was making fish-out of water gasping and turning blue around the gills. He was about to stop breathing, just like the first man.

I intubated this "fish" and Nurse Sharon began squeezing the bag, pushing oxygen into him. The blue tint of his skin, cyanosis due to lack of oxygen, changed back to the normal pink skin tone as she kept breathing for this patient. His cardiac monitor was normal, also. So, I had saved him from the devastating complications of hypoxia, with damage to the heart and brain.

The door to room two was closed now, the woman standing in the doorway had seen enough. I tried to shield onlookers in the ER from disturbing scenes, but the sounds carried. I wondered what alarming thoughts those sounds caused in the imaginations of the patients and their relatives. Another concern I had was to preserve the privacy and dignity of patients. In the close quarters of the ER, where staff must be able to observe patients always, privacy is difficult to maintain. And, of course, people are fascinated by the voyeuristic pleasure of watching the action, without having any personal risk. They are "rubberneckers," people who defy the nurse's orders to stay in their rooms with the doors shut when there is a crisis in the ER.

The nurses rolled both stretchers side to side in the trauma bay. This allowed close monitoring of each patient as we disrobed them for examination. Both were young males, with several layers of work clothes, long underwear, dirty, pungent smelling socks and mud encrusted work boots. There was a heavy alcohol odor mixed in with the distinct smell of sweaty bodies.

After the clothes had been removed I examined each man, looking for wounds or signs of trauma. Each had normal pupil reaction to bright light, constricting immediately and concentrically. This finding helped me to eliminate serious brain trauma as the cause of the coma. Coma is a technical medical term. A comatose patient has complete behavioral unresponsiveness to external stimulation. Neither of these patients had moved a muscle when I passed endotracheal tubes into their lungs. Normal people would fight that with coughing and trying to pull the tube out with their hands. Sticking needles into someone to draw blood or start IV's would normally cause movement, but these patients didn't pull away. Passing Foley catheters through the urethra into their bladders also was not responded to.

The blood pressure and pulse rate of each man was normal, as was the heart beat on the cardiac monitor. The rectal temperatures were only a degree cooler than the normal 98.6 degrees Fahrenheit. Even with all the blowing snow and cold temperature, these patients did not have hypothermia, which can cause coma.

I ordered a complete blood panel and several toxicology tests including alcohol, narcotics, tranquilizers, and marijuana. At the top of my list for coma in two young men was drugs and alcohol. Emergency physicians have memorized lists of differential diagnoses of coma from medical textbooks to guide treatment. As I grew more experienced in the profession, more possibilities were added to my mental lists. The explanation for the simultaneous coma in these two men could include: toxin exposure at work; some variant of murder or suicide; a severe allergic reaction; brain infection or cancer; HIV, or trauma.

When I began practicing in the ER, I started writing notes on the difficult or challenging medical cases encountered. In all these cases, the facts of the medical history were the most important part of the diagnosis. Most times, especially in severe trauma or coma, the medical history was not available or unreliable. ER docs call this frustrating state of affairs "practicing veterinary medicine."

The blood alcohol test for each man was 0.45%. Legal intoxication was 0.1% alcohol, so their tests were four times the level that the Commonwealth of Virginia considered to be drunk. I knew that chronic alcoholics have a higher tolerance to the poisonous, usually toxic, levels of the chemical, but these men were pickled, almost to death.

I admitted both men on ventilators to the ICU. Without any history, I was uncertain about how two men were brought to ER comatose.

Several days later, they were off the ventilators and had the endotracheal tubes removed. I walked up to the ICU and introduced myself and shook their hands. Ned was twenty-four, Charley was twenty-six and both had done construction work right out of high school. They were eating a hospital lunch and joked about how a cold beer would add flavor to the bland food. I laughed with them and asked them if they knew what had happened to them.

They readily admitted that they drank every day, starting at lunch. Ned started the story, "What with all the snow and ice, the boss man had us moving steel rebar into the bottom floor of the parking garage we was building next to the hotel on the river. We sat down on the concrete floor at lunch break to eat a sandwich and warm up some with wine."

Charley, couldn't help but laugh at the next part, "Some knucklehead buddies of ours had doctored our wine with grain, so we got good and drunk."

Ned finished, "We both decided a little nap after lunch would be OK, since the weather was too bad to do much work."

Neither Ned nor Charley remembered anything beyond that nap and waking up in the ICU. I spoke with John Allen, the chief of the paramedics and he filled in the other parts of the story.

Ned and Charley's pals had poured out the wine and filled their bottle with pure grain alcohol as a practical joke. They thought it was funny to see the men taking a little nap. But after a few hours, near quitting time, the jokers still had not seen their buddies. They found them "asleep," and couldn't shake them awake. They panicked and ran to the construction supervisor who had a cell phone and called 911, just in time to save their pals.

Most people who are not heavy drinkers would have stopped breathing and died from drinking that much grain alcohol. Every year some college kid dies from alcohol poisoning, but Ned and Charley just barely survived a toxic level. They survived because of constant exposure to large amounts of alcohol over a long time.

Many patients brought to the ER have alcohol addiction, plus other various addictions, as well as mental disorders, making the histories they give fictitious, fanciful, or incoherent. I learned more often the body language of the informant gave useful clues to the veracity of the story, too.

ER doctors become excellent judges of character and good detectives, hunting for that telling point in the medical history that clinches the diagnosis. This sleuthing is one of the most interesting parts of ER work, and the most fun. It is especially gratifying when the ER diagnosis makes a positive difference for a patient and their family.

Chapter 15
Frozen Day

The snowing had stopped but it was still bitterly cold. The coldest February on record for the Hampton Roads in eastern Virginia. The "Roads" are watery, part of the huge natural harbor at the mouth of the Chesapeake Bay. The region has the James River and many of its tributaries, several of which have frozen over, making a tempting playground for children not used to all this cold. A dusting of snow and icy rain has made the streets treacherous for school buses and all the schools are closed. The kids are housebound and looking for outdoor fun in the snow.

The ER had been busy with many patients who have fallen. The lady in room five, Mrs. Schulz, opened her porch door to let her dog Rusty out to do his business. Before she could remove the dog's leash, Rusty bolted, Mrs. Schulz attached. The porch surface was gleaming with a treacherous, transparent sheet of ice. Her feet went out from under her, she tried to stop from striking her head by strutting out her right hand. She landed heavily on her outstretched right hand and felt sudden pain and a snap.

Mrs. Schulz felt better after the nurses had given her a shot for pain. I examined her wrist and immediately knew the right radius bone in her wrist was broken and out of place, dislocated. She had a "silver fork" deformity, meaning the wrist was bent like a dinner fork, the fingers being where the fork's tines are. I injected the swollen fracture site with anesthetic and after it had numbed the fracture, I pulled on her right hand and slowly bent the wrist back into normal position, reducing the fracture-dislocation. I applied a "clam shell" plaster splint, cut in half to allow for residual swelling of the wrist, added a sling over her shoulder and she was ready to go home to Rusty.

I was applying another wrist splint to a patient who had fallen when the paramedics called on the radio, "We have a child who fell through the ice, five minutes ETA!"

I heard the diesel engine of the EMS truck drive up to ambulance bay, then the sliding doors open, followed by running feet. John Allen, the chief of the paramedics, ran to the trauma bay with a limp child in his arms.

The child's clothes were soaking wet, cold seawater dripped off his blue skin onto the floor. The little boy's head lolled back like a rag doll, with deep blue face, lips and open mouth spilling out greenish water. His skin was cold to the touch as we cut away all the wet clothes and dropped them on the floor. The ER nurses, Francis and LuAnn dried his skin and wrapped him in a warming blanket. I started chest compressions, but I thought the child was dead. My mind was racing, and I put aside the thought

of giving terrible news to his parents. I remembered a useful ER Pearl. *You're not dead until you're warm and dead!*

It was true that the medical literature reported that people had survived profound hypothermia with core body temperatures of 94 degrees. As I continued trying to get blood circulating by chest compression, Nurse Francis reported the child's rectal temperature was ninety-two degrees.

I put my stethoscope on his little chest and heard a faint heartbeat, like a little bird in a cage trying to fly away. I started an IV in his arm with warmed saline running. Nurse LuAnn had the crash cart at the bedside and I found the pediatric laryngoscope and child-sized endotracheal tubes. Chest compressions were stopped for thirty seconds as I opened the child's mouth and looked in with the light on the front of the laryngoscope. I was relieved to find no seaweed or water in his airway. I figured that his glottis, his airway, had slammed shut as a protective reflex from the shock of the frigid water as he went under. I passed the child sized endotracheal tube, secured it and then attached the tube to the ventilator. I said a prayer for him and asked the respiratory tech to warm the air going into the child. Francis passed a Foley urinary catheter and began irrigating the child's bladder with warmed saline solution. All these life-saving steps were done with skill and care by the ER team, and done spontaneously. We are all parents of young children and want this little boy to live.

Frozen Day

One of the cardiologists was in the hospital and came down to the ER to pitch in. I had not paged him. He rushed downstairs after hearing about it on the hospital grapevine. Bad news traveled fast. Warming up a cold heart is tricky, do it too slowly and the heart stays frozen forever. If you rewarm the heart too fast, it will often go into ventricular fibrillation, the chaotic lethal arrhythmia where the heart muscle looks like a bag of big worms, all wriggling together, and no coordinated heartbeat.

The faint heartbeat I heard in the child's chest had stopped. It was cardiac stand still. The ER staff continued with chest compressions and ventilation as I took a blood sample from the child's femoral artery in the groin. The arterial blood was very acidic with excess carbon dioxide and lactic acid, both metabolic toxins from the child's cold-water immersion and respiratory arrest. This acid build-up had stopped his cold heart. I ordered intravenous sodium bicarbonate, the same chemical people take for excess stomach acid, to reduce the child's blood acid.

The cardiologist who volunteered recommended we contact the pediatric intensive care specialists at the Children's Hospital. Carol, our ER unit secretary, got the intensivist on the phone. The advice included recommendation for an intravenous buffer solution to correct the child's dangerous acid build-up.

I continued CPR, gave the recommended buffer, and watched the child's rectal temperature come up to 94 degrees, a hopeful sign. The child's heart had started beating again, but no blood pressure or other signs of life.

The pediatric transport team took over from us as they moved the little boy from our ER stretcher to theirs. All of us who had worked so hard to save this child walked outside to the ambulance bay to see him off to the Children's Hospital.

I saw my breath in the cold air and shivered as the transport truck drove away.

Several days passed with no report from the Children's Hospital. I had spoken to John Allen, the head of the paramedics, when he was in the ER. John said, "The little boy's name is Royal Davis. We were called to the creek by a storekeeper calling 911. Royal's brother ran to the store when the ice gave out. Delbert and Royal had been trying to skate with tennis shoes. Delbert's shoe came off and he sat on the bank to tie his laces when he saw his brother go under the water. They live with their mom."

I called to the Pediatric ICU, identified myself, and asked for a report of child Royal Davis. The nurse came on the phone and I could tell she was smiling when she told me that the child was talking and eating his lunch.

I shared this report to the nurses, who were worried about "the little popsicle." I hoped that the hospital grapevine spread the good news.

Post Script: Since Royal's awful accident and others like it, important advances have been made in the science of human hypothermia. Deliberate, careful lowering of the core body temperature has been shown to improve the outcome in cardiac arrest victims whose stopped heart began beating by itself. Not only does hypothermia help the heart, but importantly it seems to save the brain, too.

Chapter 16
House Fire

Wintertime in the ER brought many patients injured in car accidents on the icy roads. People slipped and fell on their own steps, breaking wrists, ankles, and hips. Children, with absent or uncaring parents, got into mischief on the snowy streets and icy creeks. But there was another danger right inside their doors. That danger began when heating systems malfunctioned, and homes caught fire.

It was 3 AM and the paramedics were on the line. They had been to a house fire and were in route to the ER with a survivor. I had little time to collect my thoughts when I heard the distinctive diesel rumble of EMS-1 outside. The ambulance doors glided open and the smell hit me. The unforgettable stench of smoke and burned bacon-the unmistakable putrid odor of burned human flesh. Immediately, I am a junior medical student again, trying to overcome my repulsion and fear as I looked at Hilda Bryant for the first time. She had somehow survived the fire caused by the ignited gasoline thrown onto her by her vicious, drunk husband.

I shook off those thoughts and asked John Allen, the paramedic chief, for history.

"The pumper truck had put out the fire and the firemen had entered the small home," he explained. "They found the charred tricycle and a lawn mower in the garage. The fire fighters suspect that the fire started in bad house wiring, sparking and igniting gasoline in the lawn mower, then spreading through the insulation. The family was sleeping when neighbors saw the blaze and called 911. The house was totally engulfed with fire when the pumper got to the scene, they couldn't save it. They found this man crawling on the front yard and called for EMS back up."

The medics had gotten an effective IV in the arm of the burned man. He was almost naked, and his burned flesh was still smoking. The ER nurse cut off the hot clothes that had remained on the body, the flesh and cloth had been seared together. I saw that removing these pieces of burned clothing also removed his skin. My fingers trembled, just like they had when I had to debride Hilda Bryant's burned flesh. Hilda had been awake and aware when I clumsily cut away dead tissue from her body, this man was not awake. I had prayed he remained unconscious as I tore away the adherent cloth.

He began a low moan which drew my attention to his face. Or, more accurately, what was left of his face. His facial features were deeply charred. The cheekbones and the empty right eye socket were exposed. The white bones of his face were blackened and steaming. His scalp was exposed in several places where his hair had been burned. That stench of burned human hair stopped me for a few seconds, nausea passing quickly. His nose and both ears were gone, giving him a hideous aspect. The fire had burned his lips, and his mouth was distorted in a silent scream of pain. The teeth were bright white, shining under the spotlights in the trauma bay. Those teeth added the macabre appearance of a Halloween monster, a repellent thought that came to me, unbidden, during my examination.

As I listened to his chest and heart with my stethoscope I saw the paramedics recoil from the patient. These medics, cross-trained as fire fighters, were sweating with fear. Their eyes opened wide as they stared at their worst nightmare, burns all over the face and body. Such extensive burns they had told me left the victim more dead than alive, with a face even his own mother would be repelled by.

I knew these burns were beyond my help, but I had to try. The medics and I, wearing surgical gloves, tried to move him off the EMS stretcher onto the ER stretcher and we missed. His skin was coming off in large patches and we lost our grip. We dropped him. The thud sound as he slipped through our hands and landed on the floor sickened us all.

We bent down and quickly picked him up. He was a big man, but our shared embarrassment at our blunder gave us temporary superhuman strength. We almost threw him off the other side of the ER stretcher.

He groaned again and stopped breathing. Without thought, like a reflex, I opened his mouth, positioned his head with neck extended into the "sniffing position." This position aligns the mouth, throat, and trachea into a straight line. I advanced the lighted laryngoscope and saw soot in his mouth, throat, and airway. He had breathed fire. He was burned inside his lungs as well as his body. I place the endotracheal tube to assist his breathing.

There was not much hope for survival with these injuries, I reflected. And, who would want to survive this? I remember Hilda Bryant and her bitter will to survive, driven by revenge. But this patient has lost his entire family, a wife and a little child riding a tricycle. This tragedy was caused by an accident, not by an evil deed. The sadness was overwhelming for the ER team.

I knew there was not much more I could do for him now. He had a slim chance at a Burn Treatment Center, no chance at my hospital. I had secured his airway and was bagging oxygen into his burned lungs. The medics had started the IV in the field; my next step in trauma care was to put a Foley catheter into his urinary bladder to measure fluid output. I was stunned when I saw that his penis had melted, blocking the passage to his bladder. I could not find the urethral orifice. It was gone.

I asked the nurse to push fifteen milligrams of morphine into the IV. I could, at the very least, dull any consciousness of pain and suffering. Lord knows, there wasn't much else I could do for him.

The quiet of the winter morning was broken by the whooping sound of the transport helicopter coming down to the hospital landing pad. I had called the Burn Center surgeon who had accepted the transfer and sent the bird for the patient.

The nurses covered the patient with sterile sheets and a blanket. Then we rolled the stretcher out the ambulance bay doors, down the ramp onto the grass toward the idling helicopter with its blades rotating. I noted that it must have sleeted in the night as the wheels of the stretcher crunched and left deep ruts on the ground as we struggled to move ahead.

The helicopter downdraft was throwing icy dirt into our faces and onto the patient we were bagging. Using a transport roller, I helped the flight nurse and the ER nurse slide the patient inside. The flight nurse flinched when she saw the patient's ruined face as I squeezed the bag one last time and handed the bag to her to continue. She saw the look of sadness on our faces and nodded.

As the ER nurse and I watched, the helicopter's engine roared, lifting off with our burned patient, more dirt spraying onto our upturned faces. Tonight, he was ascending into the cold night air, perhaps to heaven.

Chapter 17
Spring

The miserable winter was finally over and the tempo in the ER had increased. Now there were more home accidents coming in for treatment. People were cutting off toes with lawn mowers, nipping fingers with hedge trimmers, and throwing stone chips off power edgers into shins. I had finished picking shards of those chipped rock out of a deep laceration on a man's leg, when I heard the radio call of EMS responding to a motorcycle accident.

Driving powerful motorcycles fast on curving highways was another rite of spring, bringing us many injured riders. Most of these motorcyclists were first-timers who wanted the thrill of bending the machine around a hairpin turn, too inexperienced to keep control of it.

I got the last chips out, irrigated the wound and closed with nylon sutures, to be removed in ten days. Then I saw John Allen, the paramedic, who beckoned me over to the EMS stretcher and the injured motorcyclist. In private, he filled me in on the details, "Doc, some of his buddies called 911. One of the guys admitted they all had been drinking beer and decided to race their bikes on the big curve. Junior had a new bike and set off fast, throwing gravel on his pals. They saw it when he lost it and called us. We had to use the power winch to lower the basket to get this guy. It was hairy. We lowered Mike Phillips down, he's our smallest medic. Mike got the guy packaged, into the basket, and we used the EMS-1 engine to reel him in." He paused then continued.

"The motorcycle lay at the bottom of a ravine and we found the rider thirty feet down the steep bank tangled in the brush. It looked to me that he had missed the turn, hit the solid metal guard rail. He and the bike sailed over the rail, tumbling down the ravine. We saw blood on the bent guard rail, where he hit it with his leg. The left leg was dangling when we loaded him in the unit. His helmet probably saved his life."

Junior was awake but so intoxicated that he couldn't answer us coherently. His jeans were torn and stained with grass. Dirt and small broken pieces of bushes fell off his clothes. His left leg was turned at an unnatural angle, his booted foot pointed almost backwards. With the trauma patient, the most obvious injury draws attention immediately, but it may not be the only threat to life. The mechanism of injury is extremely important. When the How of the injury is known, the What and Where follow. With Junior, I looked for the injury pattern associated with riders thrown from a speeding motorcycle. The forces on a body hurled off of a fast-moving vehicle can break legs, hips, pelvis, back, and neck. The internal injuries can include broken ribs, collapsed lungs, ruptured spleen, and ruptured urinary bladder. The helmet could prevent injuries to the face, scalp and head, but it's not perfect. Another complication was the patient's mental status. Was he drunk or brain injured? He was not able to guide my examination by telling me where he had pain, adding to the confusion of the accident and increasing the difficulty in his ER care. His youth was a plus, he probably didn't have chronic illnesses or take medications, but without a thorough medical history, I wasn't certain.

Nurse Janet used the heavy-duty rescue shears to cut away his jeans and boots, while I kept his helmeted head and neck from moving. I stood at the head of the patient, watching his lungs expand symmetrically, seeing his flat stomach with no expanding masses, and smelling the beer fumes with each breath.

With the clothes cut off I saw the damage to the left leg clearly. The broken, sharp edges of the tibia, the big shinbone, protruded through the skin. The bone marrow was opened, and blood was oozing with chips of bone and yellow fat globules. His left ankle and foot were flopped over and wobbled as the nurse removed his left boot. I checked his pulses from the groin down to the feet. The left leg pulses were present but diminished. I moved his knees, looking for any injury, moving them through flexion, extension, and testing the ligaments on each side. Junior's knees appeared stable with only some road rash, skin rubbed raw from sliding on the asphalt, just before his bike took him over the guard rail into the ravine below.

I rocked his hips and pelvis side to side. They felt solid. Pelvic and hip fractures bleed massively into the joints and are hard to detect early on. These hemorrhages can rapidly become fatal if blood is not replaced by transfusion quickly. Janet checked his blood pressure and heart rate and attached the cardiac monitor leads. Junior's vital signs remained steady and I drew blood for type and crossmatch for the lab just in case it might be needed.

His belly was soft and there were no chest or rib injuries seen or felt when we cut off his leather riding jacket. Any bleeding might show up later, so the trauma examinations are done serially; the initial survey found the left leg injury, other, repeated exams would be done to identify other life threats. To an outside observer, the actions Nurse Janet and I had done for

Junior might seem like a chaotic series of odd motions, but to the knowledgeable, it was like a highly choreographed, well-rehearsed ballet to save a young man's life.

The paramedics had started two IV's in the field, running a liter of saline, about a quart, into Junior. All that fluid had to go somewhere, and I asked Janet to open the sterile Foley catheter kit for me.

I passed the catheter easily and was relieved to see the clear urine return into the collection bag. Blood in the urine from a trauma patient could mean kidney, ureter, bladder, or urethral injuries.

The next step was to remove Junior's motorcycle helmet. It was a two-person procedure to prevent spinal cord damage. Janet steadied his head and neck as I spread apart the ear parts of the dented and scratched helmet, slowly lifting it off the head and over his face. I ran my fingers over his scalp and down his spine, feeling for deformities. His eyes were open and he had nystagmus, the jumpy eye movements, seen with intoxication and with brain injury. I carefully pressed my fingers on his face and along his jaw. Janet applied the hard, cervical collar to brace his neck from movement. It's a clamshell design with one part slipped behind the neck first, then the front part, under Junior's chin was fastened with Velcro straps. This collar prevented him from bending or twisting his neck. Experience with intoxicated patients had made me cautious, since Junior's neck could be broken, despite normal cervical spine x-rays. The x-rays can show damage to the bones, but not to the soft tissues of the spinal cord and brain. The hard-cervical collar would protect his spine from any sudden head movements.

The ER secretary had called for portable x-rays. I wanted to continue evaluating Junior and didn't want him to leave my sight to be transported to Radiology. There are many killers of trauma patients that sneak up unobserved and I wanted to catch them all.

Several other patients waited in the ER now, all my responsibility. The ER nurses kept me posted on the progress of patients undergoing work-ups and told me the consensus guess was "point three." This is a game played in all ERs to guess the level of alcohol in a patient. They were right on the mark. The lab reported his blood alcohol was 0.28, which level is over twice the legal limit for drunk driving in Virginia. The high alcohol level helped explain Junior's behavior, but in the trauma center I've learned to look carefully at mental impairment. Alcohol intoxication was associated with brain injury frequently, especially in high speed motor vehicle accidents. Overlooking that possibility was one trauma pitfall I won't fall into this time.

I started antibiotics and consulted the Orthopedic surgeon. After his evaluation in the ER, the surgeon wanted me to contact the patient's parents or family. The nurse handed me Junior's wallet from his jean pocket. His parents lived out of state and the phone number was no good. I charted the phone number and the time of the call, should notification become an issue later. My concern was that the impaired patient cannot give informed consent for surgery. I noted in the medical record that this was a life and limb emergency and to do nothing would be dangerous.

The orthopedic surgeon agreed and took the injured motorcyclist to the operating room to save the patient's leg. The surgeon and I knew, just looking at the extent of the damage to Junior's leg, much like a war wound, that it would probably have to be amputated.

The surgeon did his best that night, cleaning the wound, and splinting the leg. He did not remove the leg, wanting to discuss this with the patient and family. The parents were finally contacted and traveled from another state to the hospital. Junior sobered up and, after some heart-rending discussion, knew that his leg could not be saved. He agreed to the amputation. The surgeon told me later that he salvaged as much viable tissue as he could and performed a left below-the-knee amputation. The surgeon knew that this gave Junior the best possible result for walking again with a below-the-knee prosthesis.

Many months later, when the orthopedic surgeon came to ER for another patient, he filled me in on how Junior did.

"He did well after the amputation, being fitted for the prosthetic limb within a week. He did all the physical therapy just fine and when I saw him in the office the last visit he looked good. He walked well and wanted me to release him from care. He told me that he had gotten enough money from the insurance settlement to buy a new motorcycle but decided to go back to college with the money, instead. I was surprised by that and asked Junior what he was going to study. He said,

"I want to be a paramedic; those guys saved my life."

I knew many physicians, nurses, and paramedics who changed their life direction after surviving experiences like the one that Junior had endured. Facing injury or illness can build in a person an internal resilience and a powerful motivation to help others. I saw that motivation in action every day in the ER. It's a wonder that anyone would want to be subject to the stresses of a job in the ER. Shift work, seeing people at their worst, dealing with trauma especially effecting children, missing many holidays with family, low pay, and few job benefits are just some of those stresses. The chance to make a positive change in a stranger's life is what keeps ER staff energized, ignoring the personal hardship and sacrifices. It was what kept me eager to go to work in the ER, too.

Chapter 18
A Cough and A Decision

How can the ER doc, pulled in many different directions, make sound decisions about patients seen only once? How can order be wrung from the emergency department chaos?

I'll reveal some of what I've learned in my career in emergency medicine. Grandmaster chess players, concert pianists, and even stand-up comedians learn to see patterns in their work. They have taught themselves to see the deeper structures in games, music, and laughter.

Doctors also must teach themselves to find the hidden causes of a patient's distress.

It starts in medical school, where you are taught that many symptoms form a pattern. The professors told the students, "Push and squeeze to make it one disease!" This teaching helped me to understand how the varied patient experiences could be the manifestations of a single disease. But, early in my career, I learned that patients and diseases don't fit into a single mold, "Patients can have as many diseases as they please!"

Then another old saw I heard while on the wards, "Common diseases are common, uncommon diseases are uncommon." My first instructor in the ER opined, "If you hear hoof beats, think horses, not zebras!" After a few years practicing I added a corollary to that: "There are very few unicorns stomping about, but they exist!"

The idea in all these aphorisms was the reality of the great diversity of patient presentations. Even simple sounding symptoms like a cough could have many causes and different treatments. As I gained experience treating life-threatening conditions, I saw many patterns. These patterns had been refined into national protocols, like the Advanced Trauma Life Support course designed by the American College of Surgeons and the Advanced Cardiac Life Support course by the American Heart Association. Both courses became a mandatory part of the emergency physician's post-graduate education and have reduced suffering and saved many lives. But, they are "cookbook" approaches to reducing indecision in crises. They are necessary, but not sufficient to practice in the ER.

I learned the trade in the same way that grandmasters, musicians, and all performers learned their skills. All professional students start with trial and error, corrected by experts. Doctors in training, under supervision, practiced a lot, perfecting what had been taught. At some point, my thoughts and actions became instinctual, the performance flowing without pause. I recognized many patterns of illness and injury in the ER patients and could respond without hesitation.

My Professor stressed that the patient would tell you the diagnosis only if you paid attention. Learning to listen actively to the patient and family was important to him. His example was one of kindness and interest in the patient as a person with an illness. He somehow could elicit key points from the patient that lead to successful treatment. He pointed out changes in the patient's face and body language that helped me understand the real message in the words spoken.

I later learned to think about my own thinking, especially

when dealing with threatening, angry, or mentally unstable ER patients. The key to the care of the patient is caring for that person. This is a simple formulation that takes a lifetime in the ER to learn.

Patients presenting to the ER often are in pain or frightened, especially when they give their history to the admitting clerks. The triage RN takes that initial history and records the vital signs, often guiding the patient to put his complaint into a coherent formulation. The man who sat at her desk told her, "Nurse, I have a cough and just want better cough medicine tonight."

The patient was brought back to an examining room and responded to the ER nurse's question with more information, his story more complete.

"I coughed up blood tonight and my girlfriend got scared, so here I am."

He also told the ER nurse that he was an off-duty policeman.

It was half past one in the morning in the ER and there was a lull in the tempo. There is little rhyme or reason in the arrival of patients, although the weekends bring more traffic accidents from the combination of drinking and driving. But this night shift was less frantic, the last patient had been admitted twenty minutes ago. So, when the ER nurse told me that there was a policeman coughing, I walked over to see what sounded like a straightforward case of a cold, maybe bronchitis. I noted that his story had changed from the triage nurse to the ER nurse, adding the bloody sputum. Frequently patients change what they tell the ER nurses and then the doctor; usually it is fear, rarely deception with the dishonest intent to get time off from work or to get drugs. Patients will tell what's really bothering them to the nurse or doctor whom they feel cares about them.

It was my policy to see any peace officer or court officer quickly, bumping them to the front of the line, ahead of other patients except trauma or people in severe pain. It made good sense to offer this courtesy, a small favor for the many times they had responded to trouble in the ER, arresting threatening or violent people, protecting me and the staff.

I introduced myself and shook hands with Carl Alston. He was in his mid-forties with the beefy nose and dilated veins in his red cheeks I associated with alcoholism. He admitted to a two-pack-a-day smoking habit. I didn't smell alcohol on his breath, but there was the sharp, bitter smell of tobacco in the air. He was taking an antidepressant. He told me that he has had a bad cough for a week, not getting better with over-the-counter cough medicines. He has been coughing up yellow colored mucus. When asked by the triage nurse, he had, at first denied seeing blood in the sputum, a fact that would indicate serious lung disease.

"Doc, if you could just give me something stronger for this cough, I'll be on my way," Carl said. He wanted to get out of the ER fast and I picked up on his fear as well as anxiety. I know men hate to go to doctors, which is probably why he had come to the ER after midnight, it represented a loss of masculine control. I must tread lightly to treat him, something told me that this was not just an annoying cough. I felt that Carl didn't think it was a cold, either.

I asked him about the antidepressant. He smiled for the first time, in control, on firm ground. He began his story in a calm, self-deprecating way. He told me that he had recently gotten divorced, and it was a bitter one. "Lots of arguing about things and money," he said in a matter-of-fact tone.

The same month that the divorce was final, his father suddenly died of a massive heart attack. His mother had died many years ago from breast cancer and he was an only child. He was then put into the stressful position of executor of his father's estate.

"I wasn't sleeping, and I was drinking more every day. The Department put me in a desk job that I hated, and I didn't know where to turn for help," Carl said. "One night, after a heavy drinking binge, I jumped off the downtown Hampton Bridge, twenty feet down into the river. The water was cold and black, felt just how my heart felt."

"I really wanted to end it all, to leave the problems behind," he said.

He told me that he didn't expect to live, but a fishing party was passing under the bridge and pulled him from the water. As luck would have it, one of his best friends was on the boat that rescued him.

That friend stayed with him and convinced him to get help. The police department psychologist examined him, and Carl was admitted to the psychiatric hospital.

"I hated the psychiatrist and the entire thing about being such a weak man. I felt all alone and broken. I was an inpatient for three weeks, and now feel like I can go on with life. And now I go to group twice a week. I never knew much about my feelings before," he said.

Carl looked at me and opened his hands wide, "My ex-wife and I came to an agreement about money and visitation. I finished settling my father's estate with the attorney and CPA, and I even got a new Department office job that looks good to me."

He smiled more broadly when he told me about his new lady-friend with whom he planned a camping trip to the mountains. "Mary is divorced and understands where I am emotionally. She's a great person and loves the outdoors. She and I want to take a tent to the Smoky Mountains for a week." He paused then continued. "If only I could shake off this cough!"

I would have given him a stronger cough pill, but something gave me pause. When I put the stethoscope to his chest the sounds were harsher than just a cold. Something else caused the coughing, that he admitted had been getting worse. Carl's remarkable improvement from suicidal to hopeful in only three weeks made me uneasy. People take months and years to process just one of the recent midlife losses Carl told me about. I suspected that he was emotionally fragile and denying his continuing sadness.

"After all, doc, I did go for a midnight swim in the river a while back," he said, too fast to be the joke he intended.

Carl didn't want me to take bloods or chest x-rays. His denial of illness was profound.

I sat down on the chair across from the stretcher and spoke to him, with what I hoped was a calm voice, removing any hint of judgment. "Carl, you've come to the ER worried about this cough, and I will give you medicine for it," I said. "But I want to get an x-ray of your lungs. I've heard sounds in your lungs that are not normal."

I gave him some stronger cough medicine and he was taken to radiology for the chest x-rays. I knew the x-rays would show disease, my secret hope was for a patch of pneumonia that could be treated with antibiotics.

Carl returned from the x-ray and was seated on the stretcher as I put the films on the lighted view box in the room. I must have given an involuntary gasp as I looked at what certainly was wide spread cancer of his lungs.

"Is it cancer, doc?"

There was almost no normal lung visible on the x-ray, it was very bad. I was torn between the need to be compassionate to a man getting the worst diagnosis possible, a nightmare delivered in the middle of the night by a stranger, and the obligation as a physician to present facts honestly. I remembered what my Professor taught me: "Be compassionate and honest with the patient, and yourself."

I was shaken and tried to do the best for Carl. He looked down at the floor when I finally said, "I can't be sure, but it is serious, and I would like to admit you to the hospital."

I had been honest, and I hoped compassionate in the way I shared this terrible news. He refused admission, but would see the Oncologist, whom I had called for him at 3 AM.

A month later I received a follow-up report on Carl. The lung biopsy showed metastatic small cell lung cancer, one of the very worst kinds. Carl had been treated with several rounds of chemotherapy with some improvement. Both of his lungs had cancer, so surgery was not an option. I did not receive further reports about his condition and suspect that he died of the cancer when it continued spreading in his body, despite the treatment.

I have often thought about Carl and that early morning ER visit. I had seen many middle-aged men with a smoker's cough who wanted cough medicine. In a busy ER, it made sense to write a prescription and give a referral for outpatient follow-up. What made me listen more closely to Carl was the feeling I had of emotional turmoil that he could not express in words. The way he told his history to first the Triage Nurse, then to the bedside ER Nurse and finally to the ER doctor, each time changing things a bit was a subtle clue to his turmoil.

The most effective clinicians I worked with knew their patients so well they could make good judgments talking to them on the phone, encouraging them to come to the ER. When I examined those patients, every time the referral doctor was correct in the assessment.

In ER, it is the usual to meet the patient for the first time. The doctor and the patient are strangers in a setting of noise, turmoil, and fear. I must make decisions for the patient, and I always started with the general question, "What has brought you to the ER?" If I can present a calm surface with polite inquiries, rather than a hurried interrogation, the patient's answers are very important for treatment, and stress is reduced for the patient and the doctor.

Part of understanding patients in the charged atmosphere of a busy ER is to know oneself and trust any emotional reaction to them. If I felt sadness after speaking with a patient, it was likely that the person was depressed. If I felt threatened or frightened after meeting a patient, it was a violent person about to lose control. Patients in a manic phase couldn't control their speech and jumpy movements and made me feel agitated too. But far and away, the emotional tone I felt most often from the patients was one of dread and fear of the unknown.

Carl spoke to me with words, but the other message he expressed wordlessly moved me to look deeper for a cause of his cough.

Chapter 19
The Hardest Thing

Ask any ER doctor "What's the hardest thing you do?" and you might be surprised at the answer. No, it's not resuscitating heart attacks. No, it's not treating gunshot wounds. And, no it's not solving medical mysteries to save a life. It is the most painful duty I have faced and have never gotten used to, telling the relatives about the death of a loved one.

I entered medical school with the dream of helping people, curing and saving them from the inevitability of death. I rotated through psychiatry as a medical student, learning about mental illness treatment, but never being taught how to speak to patients about dying or death. I saw how surgeons shut down their emotions concerning the death of a patient, viewing "the loss of a patient" as a failure. This coldness didn't seem a satisfactory example to follow, nevertheless it was accepted by and expected of trainees in Internal Medicine, as well. A death on the medical wards often was explained as the patient's fault, not a failure of treatment. I heard, "If only he had stopped smoking", or "She should have come in sooner, before it spread," as plausible explanations for the patient's death. The euphemisms usually contained in the newspaper obituaries were frequently heard, too. "He passed away in his sleep." "She went to heaven last night." "Lost a courageous battle with cancer."

When I read Dr. Sherwin Nuland's book, *How We Die*, I found some insight into my distress. He wrote that, "of all the professions, medicine is one of the most likely to attract people with high personal anxieties about dying. We became doctors because our ability to cure gives us power over the death we are so afraid." All of us deny our mortality. But I had no guidance or advice on how to get through that denial to deliver bad news.

In the Hampton Roads area of Virginia there are many bridges and two tunnels that connect the Peninsula city of Hampton with the Southside cities of Norfolk and Virginia Beach.

The EMS radio call sounded grim. I heard paramedic Mike Noland, sigh, as he continued, "Highway Patrol called us for a fatal motorcycle accident in the Hampton Roads Tunnel. The report is that a motorcyclist was passing cars in the oncoming lane and lost control. Looks like he hit the wall and a following car hit him and dragged him. Troopers are not charging the car driver, but she is shaken up and crying. She refused transport to the hospital. ETA five minutes. Out."

Mike and his crew rolled the stretcher into the trauma bay with care. The motorcyclist wore a scratched helmet and riding leathers. His eyes were closed, and his face looked unmarked. He was blue around his lips. His arms and legs were thrust out in unnatural angles. I could smell the burned rubber from the tire tracks over his crushed chest. He had no pulse or heartbeat. He wasn't breathing. His chest crunched when I put my stethoscope on it to listen for any heart sounds. All his ribs were broken and I knew his heart and lungs had been destroyed when the car ran over his body.

I looked up at Mike and the other paramedics and nodded. This young man was dead.

The nurses found a U.S. Navy photo ID in his effects. I asked the unit secretary to call the Navy Base in Norfolk. I spoke with his commanding officer. The Naval officer didn't remember him but remarked that it was common for young sailors to buy motorcycles with their first paycheck. He provided me with a phone number for the parents.

The secretary put the call through as I stood at the ER nurse's station, dreading what I had to do. Secretly I wished that the phone number was incorrect, and I wouldn't have to speak to his parents. But, I heard a voice on the phone after two rings.

I introduced myself and said I was calling from the Emergency Department in Hampton, Virginia. A female voice had answered the phone with a pleasant hello.

After ascertaining that she was his mother, I gently told her the details of the motorcycle accident, then paused. I told her that I was very sorry to inform her that her son was dead. The phone dropped with a bang on a hard surface. I heard what sounded like gasping and sobbing. A male voice picked up the line.

"Who are you? Where did you say you were calling from? What did you say happened to our son? Is he still alive? We live in Cleveland, Ohio. Will be there as soon as we can."

I wanted to offer some comfort and tell them more about the accident, but before I could say anything more, our connection was severed. Listening to that dial tone made me sad. But really, what more could I say to them? I knew nothing could soften the blow, lessen the heartache of such awful news, but I wanted to try. Imagine a stranger calling long distance, in the middle of the night, telling you that your son was dead. I can't think of anything more horrible.

Still holding the phone in my hand, I saw the nurses looking down at the floor. The ER nursing supervisor came to me and touched my arm.

"He may have been an organ donor. We must contact the team," she said. I just nodded as I put the phone back into its cradle.

I knew it was hospital protocol to contact the Organ Donation Team in traumatic deaths in the ER. This team of specially trained nurses would meet with the next of kin to answer questions and request the anatomical gift. The donated eyes, hearts, livers, kidneys, lungs, bones, and skin are the true gift of life for many sufferers. These courageous Organ Donation nurses relieve the ER staff from an awful task. The ER team shares the loss of life with the grieving family at the bedside and can't bring themselves to ask for more sacrifice of them. This motorcyclist could have been an organ donor but had not made that decision on his driver's license.

The ER supervisor contacted the team and explained the circumstances of the accident. I then spoke with the Organ Donation Team head nurse and she agreed that since the parents were traveling from a distance, it would be inappropriate to ask them to donate their son's body by a telephone call.

Several days later I saw a tall Virginia State Trooper standing at the hallway ER doors, his face drawn, and his eyes cast down at the floor. Through those doors, down that hallway and down the stairs to the hospital basement was the two-stretcher morgue. He stood with his back against one of the doors, holding it open. He held his Smokey-the-Bear hat in one hand and a large paper grocery sack in the other. I knew that paper sack held the personal effects of the motorcyclist. The Trooper had taken the parents to the morgue to identify their son's body.

An ER nurse held a middle-aged lady's hand and walked her to our small family room. A gray-haired man followed them. The nurse seated them and closed the door. She found me at the nurse's station, finishing a note on a patient's chart.

"The parents are here for you to talk with," she said in a quiet voice.

I opened the family room door and introduced myself to the couple. I had been dreading this meeting since my phone call to them telling them that their son had died. The family room is a small, secluded private space where a family waited for news.

Mr. and Mrs. Jones were in their fifties, sitting close together on the small sofa, holding hands. I was just across from them on a chair, my knees almost touching the sofa.

"I was very sorry to call you with such bad news. The paramedics brought him to the ER immediately from the accident in the tunnel." I paused to let them speak.

Mrs. Jones's eyes were red and downcast, her hands clutching a framed photograph, which she showed me.

It was a young man, smiling into the camera. He was wearing his U.S. Navy dress white uniform. His white sailor's cap tilted back on his head, arms held at his side. The beautiful Stars and Stripes behind his left shoulder. Printed below the photo was: William F. Jones, Seaman First Class, USN, flanked by the two anchors, proud symbols of the fleet.

I held the frame in my hands and felt an emotional pull. My father had served in the U.S. Navy in the Pacific during World War II, and I remembered how impossibly young he had looked in a similar photograph.

I handed the framed photograph back to the mother. Our eyes met, and she said, "Billy had always been our adventurer, jumping off a roof with a bedsheet around him when he was ten. Racing his bicycle down the hill near our house, breaking his arm in the process."

She told me this with a small smile, her eyes sparkling through her tears. Her husband put his arm over her shoulder, pulling her tight as she began to sob. He looked from her to me and quietly asked me, "Doctor, did our son suffer?"

I teared up and took a few seconds to say to these parents, both still in shock, trying to make sense of this loss.

"No sir, your son was killed instantly," I replied. "The woman driving the car that struck your son was terribly distraught, and I know she would want you to know how sad she feels about it."

Mrs. Jones, blotting the tears off her face with a tissue, continued, "Billy loved the Navy, his Commanding Officer has been very kind to us. He told us that they would be sending him home for us."

Mr. Jones squeezed her hand and they both began to weep. I sat there watching their grief. Not knowing what to do or say. I stayed with them in that small family room.

After a few minutes, they wiped their tears and stood up. Mr. Jones shook my hand and Mrs. Jones gave me a quick hug as the ER nurses walked them out of the department.

These times wore me and the ER nurses down. I never felt that I had done much to relieve the pains of loss. Grief is a heavy burden for us all, and no one knew how to lessen it for families, gripped by sudden loss of a loved one. The death of a child is especially heart-breaking, not in the natural order of life. Parents should die before their children. When that order is disrupted there can be no consolation in mere words.

I learned not to try to explain a child's death to the parents. Any words I could mutter to them at that time would sound hollow. The simple facts of a young man's death could not answer the deeper question of why he had died, now. That question haunted Billy Jones's parents then, and it haunts me still.

Chapter 20
The Smurfettes

The dayshift nurses called themselves "The Smurfettes" after the small, happy cartoon characters. Nurse Susan was the shift leader and the tallest "Smurfette," she was five-feet-two. Nurse Emmy and Nurse Barbara are shorter, just barely above five-feet tall. They have teamed up together for years and laugh about some of the weird ER cases.

Nurse Emmy told the story of her first night shift in the ER. Emmy was born in the Philippines and moved here to Virginia with her Navy husband. She was working the Triage Desk, interviewing patients as they first presented to the ER, when a man with a freshly bruised face sat down at her desk. He calmly told her how he had been injured. Upset by this Emmy jumped up and called her supervisor, Nurse Susan.

"This patient has been assaulted and he knows who did it. Should I call the police?" Emmy asked.

"What did he tell you?" Sharon questioned.

"He told me that Mr. Jack Daniels pushed him down the stairs!" Emmy said.

Emmy now knows that the patient was joking with her, referring to an adult beverage not an assailant, but it still got a smile from the other "Smurfettes."

The nurses were talking about their weekend plans when I walked over to the nurse's station, writing on a patient's chart. They were chatting about some of the unusual cases they had seen. Nurse Susan asked me if I had any stories to tell.

I told them that I was working last weekend when the unit secretary called me over to the phone. "It's a personal call, Doc, who needs to talk to you about her husband."

I picked up the phone and heard a familiar voice, Molly, a friend from Church.

"She told me that her husband, Charlie, had had a bellyache all day, had stopped eating and was now on the couch, clutching his stomach. What should she do?"

I told her to bring him to the ER and I would see him. About an hour later the Triage nurse showed Molly and Charlie to a room. Charlie looked sick, pale with a fine sheen of sweat on his face. He grimaced when he sat on the ER stretcher and took off his shirt for examination.

He had a slight fever, 101 degrees, and had some tenderness in his lower belly, otherwise it was a normal exam. He told me he had been fine over the last week. His main concern was his work truck, which was acting up.

Charlie had been working on his pick-up truck most of yesterday morning. He leaned under the hood, checked the spark plugs and distributor. He explained that he had an unlit cigarette dangling from his lips and his usual toothpick jammed in the other side of his mouth.

I asked Charlie what happened next.

"Today I replaced the plugs and points and I took the cover off the air filter. I could see that there was gas in the carburetor and it seemed to be working OK. But, no matter what I tried it wouldn't keep running. After a few minutes bending over the engine I got a sharp pain in my belly. I thought it was from too much stomach acid, what with the truck not running. So, I put the wrench down and went into the house for a Goody Powder for the pain."

Molly interrupted him, "Doc, he tried Maalox, then Tylenol and Advil, then Pepto-Bismol. Finally, he emptied a bottle of Milk of Magnesia. I got worried since he told me it hurt worse after all he took that stuff."

Charlie continued, "I felt a bit better after the Milk of Magnesia. A few minutes later it really hit me again. I doubled over and felt sick to my stomach. I told Molly to call you, and now I'm here."

I explained to Charlie and Molly that he shouldn't eat or drink anything else with stomach pain and I would need to give him intravenous fluids and get blood for lab tests. Charlie just nodded, feeling too sick to object.

I asked the nurse to draw blood for the lab and start an IV of normal saline. I sent a urine specimen since Charlie's pain could be caused by a kidney stone and blood in his urine would be a clue. Charlie's urine was crystal clear, but his white blood count was three times normal, showing mostly the type of cells that fight infection. Charlie had an abdominal infection.

I reexamined Charlie's belly with gentle pressure over the lower right side and he screamed and almost launched himself off the stretcher. I apologized for causing the pain and explained to him that this was probably appendicitis and he would need an operation today.

Charlie was now sweating and holding his belly with both hands. He readily agreed to the operation. I contacted my friend the general surgeon who whisked Charlie upstairs to the OR.

Two hours later the surgeon came down to the ER. He still

had his scrubs on, shoe protectors over his sneakers, and his surgical mask pulled down off his face. He was smiling when he gave me the report,

"Your friend had a perforated appendix, but no pus pocket, yet. Guess what I found when I got the appendix out?"

I shook my head. I really didn't have a clue.

"The appendix had a toothpick sticking out of it!"

Charlie made a quick recovery and was home in two days.

Several weeks later, at Church, Molly thanked me for my help. She told me that Charlie was back at work, feeling fine. She was relieved and laughed as we spoke together. "You know how he was working on that stupid truck that was broken? While he was in the hospital I had the truck towed into the dealership. The mechanic called me that he had found the problem and the truck engine ran fine. He took the carburetor apart. It was jammed with a toothpick."

I think Charlie was so intent on fixing his truck that he swallowed a toothpick without realizing it. He carried toothpicks in his shirt pocket, next to those cigarettes he was trying to quit smoking, and some of them fell into the truck's engine while he was leaning over, landing in the carburetor.

The "Head Smurfette" Nurse Susan, summed it up,

"Who says toothpicks are cheap?"

Chapter 21
The Smurfettes versus Godzilla

"Get him restrained," I shouted as the nurses and I struggled to prevent a very big, very strong man from rolling off the stretcher onto the floor. "Call Security to help us!"

The patient outweighed the entire ER dayshift -- The Smurfettes and me. Each nurse grabbed an arm or leg to hold him down. I tried to hold his head to keep it from banging into the side rails. He thrashed his head side to side, and I lost my grip. The nurses were lifted off their feet as he bucked and twisted, but they held on. It was like the science fiction movie where people were tossed aside by the radioactive monster, Godzilla. And Godzilla seemed to be winning. It was a losing battle until the ER hall doors opened and four security guards ran to the bedside. Each of the security men was well over six feet tall and powerful. They joined the struggle and finally could hold him down. I broke out in sweat and my heart pounded with the effort. The nurse's hair flew around her head as we forced the wild man into restraints.

He howled, making inhuman sounds that raised the hair on the back of my neck. It took all our combined strength to hold his legs down and fasten the three-inch wide leather straps around his thick ankles. Nurse Barbara, one of the Smurfettes, slipped the straps through the stretcher fittings and pulled them tight. Nurse Emmy, another petite Smurfette, tightened the leather straps on each of the big man's thick wrists.

As Barbara fastened the last leather strap, she wiped the sweat off her brow and said, "Doc, the paramedics and the Hampton Police had to rush to another call, so I jotted down what they told me at the triage desk."

The stretcher rocked side-to-side with the restrained patient still making incoherent, animal sounds. The man ground his teeth and spit. Now I was worried that he might turn the stretcher over in his violent thrashing. The trauma stretcher was solid, state-of-the art, built of stainless tube steel, riding on heavy solid rubber wheels, which were locked in place to prevent rolling. Built like a tank and cost $15,000. It was rated to carry four hundred fifty pounds and designed so well that even a Smurfette could move a patient by herself.

The man rocked the wheels up off the floor a good three inches with each scream. Whatever he had taken to get into this state did not lessen his strength. I stood back in awe watching him as I caught my breath.

Sweat poured off him and he had a peculiar body odor. It was cloying, an unpleasant, chemical scent. Each time he opened his mouth to scream, another wave of foul air seemed to cover me. His eyes were bulging and unseeing, wandering back and forth. I knew this abnormal eye movement, coarse horizontal nystagmus, was a sure sign of toxin exposure or drugs, especially the ones that cause acute psychosis, like this patient had.

Nurse Barbara continued, "The Hampton police told me that they were called for a disturbance in the neighborhood. They found this man wandering in the middle of the street without his pants on. When the cops told him to stop, he ran into a hedge and fell into a lady's flowerbed."

They cuffed him and called for the ambulance. They said that the man didn't resist, just kept shouting some gibberish in a loud angry voice. The medics moved him from the ambulance to our stretcher and that's when the monster showed up.

Over the next hour, the "monster" calmed. He had shut his eyes, but they still jumped under his closed eyelids. He took progressively deeper breaths, followed by a pause wherein he stopped breathing. A few seconds later he started breathing again. I had seen this Cheyne-Stokes respiration pattern before, when I had rotated through Neurology as a medical student, it meant that the patient still had toxin or drugs in his system, affecting his brain.

He didn't seem to feel my needle stick to draw blood. He didn't flinch or draw back his hand. I handed the blood tubes to Emmy who placed them in the pneumatic tube system which took the specimens to the lab for testing. I leaned over the stretcher railing to speak to the patient. That's when my tie brushed the back of his hand, and he gripped it in his powerful hands. He pulled my tie and my head followed, down to six inches from his face. I was unable to free myself, using all my strength with both hands to loosen his grip. His eyes were still closed, and he seemed asleep, but I was frantic.

I shouted, and the nurses rushed to help. Nurse Emmy cut my tie with her bulky bandage scissors, releasing me. The patient didn't respond to my shouts or movement as I pushed away from the stretcher in relief.

The laboratory toxicology screens were not helpful in arriving at a diagnosis for the patient's initial psychotic behavior followed by his somnolence. There was no evidence of marijuana, which can cause psychosis. The tests for narcotics, or benzodiazepine were negative. There was no alcohol in his blood, either.

I ordered intravenous fluids for the patient and an hour before the end of my twelve-hour shift he was more coherent. The Smurfettes released all the restraints from Godzilla's ankles and wrists. I offered him water to drink and sat next to his stretcher to speak with him. I had slipped off my tie that had been cut and tossed it into the trash can.

"The police and the paramedics brought you here several hours ago," I asked. "Do you remember what happened to you?"

His voice was hoarse, and he had to drink some water to respond, "I been over to a friend's house for a party," he said. "Some dude offered me some acid, but I doan do that shit. Some other dude was passing a toke, so I smoked some of his reefer. The next thing I remember was some cop sitting on me, cuffing me."

I told him that the police had found him walking in the street barefoot, with no pants on.

"Doc that was some bad stuff," he said. "I doan remember taking my shoes and pants off at all."

He told me his name was Arthur Washington and he worked in the Newport News Shipyard. He admitted that he smoked marijuana and drank some beer on the weekend, but adamantly denied using any other drugs.

I walked Arthur around in the ER. He was steady and wanted to go home. I asked Nurse Barbara to take out his IV and give him a set of scrubs to wear home until he found his pants.

Arthur gave me his home phone number. Nurse Emmy spoke to his wife who came to the hospital to pick him up.

As he was leaving the ER with his wife, I pulled him aside and said, "Arthur that stuff made you into a real monster, like Godzilla, and you scared us."

He looked down at the floor and said, "Please tell the nurses I'm ashamed of myself. I hope I didn't hurt nobody."

I shook his hand and said, "You didn't hurt anyone; the only casualty was my tie."

He was bewildered by that, but before he could say more, his wife pulled him away.

The Smurfettes versus Godzilla

That Christmas, the Smurfettes told me they had a present for me. Months had passed, and I had forgotten about Arthur. I opened a little package and saw the two ends of my tie.

The Smurfettes had a good laugh at my expense.

And that was the very last time I wore a necktie to work in the ER.

Chapter 22
Peter Rabbit

"Two children down, fifteen minutes out, coming to you." The radio barked, and it was the paramedics with really bad news. They called from a moving ambulance, the call given in rapid fire, the pitch in the speaker's voice rising.

They were at a distance from the hospital having answered the call in an upscale neighborhood, miles from our ER location which was in a gritty part of town. Many of the hospital physicians and nurses lived in that section of the city, where they raised their families in an environment of comfort and safety. I never had life-threatening calls from that part of town and it was unsettling to hear the distress in the paramedic's voice.

What could this mean? I worried that it might be children injured in a house fire. Possibly a smoke alarm malfunctioned, and carbon monoxide built up to toxic levels, hurting sleeping kids. I was dismayed by the thought of a home invasion. Could an intruder hurt little children in a panic to steal things from a fine home?

These things probably entered the thoughts of the night ER nurses, Jean and Delores, too. The nurses and I put aside concerns and started preparations for two victims, opening packages of IV fluids and child sized needles. I checked the laryngoscope, a stainless-steel handle attached to a folding spoon-shaped blade used to hold the tongue out of the way, while threading an endotracheal tube into the airway. I snapped it open to ensure that the battery light was bright, then I paused to check my own pulse as I detached the six-inch adult blade, set it aside, and attached the three-inch blade, designed for children.

And now we waited, anxiously. Six minutes crawled by and I called the paramedics on the radio for an update. The nurses and I were stunned when they responded, "Both children in full arrest, CPR, IV's started.

In a minute or two, the ambulance roared into the ER bay. The automatic doors slid open and the paramedics ran, pushing their stretcher. One of the men was astride the rolling stretcher, pumping the chest of one small child, then shifting to do cardiopulmonary compressions on the other child's chest. I saw that both little heads rolled side to side as the stretcher was pushed to the trauma beds. The paramedic doing the CPR, was a recent graduate of the class I had helped teach at the Fire Department Academy. Sweat poured off his face and he nodded to me as I helped lift the little bodies onto the ER stretchers.

The first child was a chunky toddler in a Peter Rabbit zip-up pajama set. His lips and face were a deep blue, and he was not breathing. Nurse Jean took over from Charlie and began chest compressions. Nurse Delores fitted an oxygen mask over the child's mouth and began squeezing the football shaped Ambu bag, giving artificial respiration. The little boy's chest rose and fell with each puff of oxygen Delores gave. I listened to his chest, but there was no heart-beat. I ordered intravenous epinephrine, a powerful heart stimulant and continued chest compressions. I plunged a needle into his right femoral artery and drew back dark blood. Normally that arterial blood would have been red, rich with circulating oxygen. The test results on this child's arterial blood were dismal. The blood was acidotic, meaning that he has not been breathing for several minutes. I knew that his chances for survival were dim, but perhaps I could increase them. I said a silent prayer for the child, placed the laryngoscope into his mouth, lifted the tongue and passed a child-sized endotracheal tube into place. I hoped that delivering oxygen to his lungs directly would correct the blood acidosis faster.

Nurse Delores continued pushing oxygen into his little lungs, Charlie had taken over the cardiac compressions from Nurse Jean, who then helped me with the other child.

The second child, a bit larger than the first, was not breathing. I intubated him and continued chest compressions. Nurse Jean's hands shook as she connected the endotracheal tube to an Ambu bag and began pumping oxygen into this little boy's lungs. Tears rolled down Jean's cheeks as she continued doing her job to help the patient. I remembered that she had a very sick young child at home. She had told her ER friends about chemotherapy. I knew that dark thoughts were torturing her, but I needed her to focus on our task.

"Jean, I know this is hard, please stay and help them. I need you here," I whispered.

She wiped her eyes and nodded. She took the Ambu bag from me and continued squeezing oxygen into that tiny body that could be her own little son.

I ordered epinephrine, continued cardiopulmonary resuscitation, but it didn't help. The little hearts were just not coming back to life. These little boys have gone down that final pathway together and I could not bring them back. My mind was racing. I must have something else to try, something heroic, something desperate. I sprayed epinephrine down the endotracheal tubes into the highly vascular lungs in the attempt to get their hearts beating again. This was an accepted procedure that often works when everything else failed, but not this time.

But I couldn't just give up. They were too young to be dead. This can't be natural. They were well-formed and cared for. They didn't have the appearance of abuse. They were clean with no bruises or wounds. Their Peter Rabbit pajamas were neat and clean. Someone must have loved them.

I silently prayed for their lives and continued CPR, but despite our efforts over twenty minutes, they were both dead. I shined light into their little eyes. The pupils were widely dilated and fixed, would not move with the light. This meant that their brains were gone.

They won't see playschool. They won't have any more birthday parties. They won't play round the Christmas tree ever again. And now, with my heart full of dread, I must tell the family.

The ER had a small room with a closed door where we asked

relatives of the stricken to wait. It had a small couch and two armchairs. The lamps on the side tables were kept low, giving the space a subdued light. Just off the busy ER, with its sights and sounds, the room had a hushed, expectant atmosphere. Each table had open boxes of tissues.

As Nurse Delores and I entered the room together, we saw Grandma, who was seated, holding a man around the shoulders. He was the children's father, sobbing and rocking in her arms, his eyes cast down in grief. Grandma's knowing eyes ran over the nurse and me, searching for a glimmer of hope. Her eyes came to rest on my face and she immediately began to rock back and forth, her cheeks wet.

I sat down in the small chair across from them, heart sick, reflecting on how many times I have had to give relatives the news of loss, usually adults dying from heart attacks or trauma. It was always a shock to those relatives. All of us build up a wall of denial of loss, even with loved ones suffering from terminal illnesses, whose death is expected. But the death of a child, and here, the death of two children, was the worst possible news that any ER doctor had to give to a family. Nothing on this earth prepared me for this duty. I knew that this would be another emotional scar on my battered soul, an unavoidable pain that must be endured, forever.

I held Grandma's hand in mine, and told them gently that the boys are gone, passed away. These last words hit her and her son like a club. I took a deep breath and continued, "Where is their mother?"

My question was met with silence. Their father, sobbing, looked up at me with tear-streaked eyes, avoiding the question. I saw flashes of anger in that look. Grandma clutched his hands, in a gesture to keep him seated next to her. She was a bit more composed when she said to me and the nurse, "Thank you for trying to save my grandsons."

I touched her hands and stood to leave this small room, the grief so deep, I had trouble breathing.

I excused myself from the room, allowing the nurse to speak with them. I knew that Nurse Delores was taking this duty on to spare Nurse Jean, who sat at the ER nurse's station, with her head bowed. Delores asked them the awful post-mortem questions she hated to ask. Do you have a minister? Do you have a funeral home? What is to be done with the personal effects? And, the worst possible information was given last. We cannot release their bodies to you now. As in all suspicious deaths, their little bodies must be turned over to the State Medical Examiner to determine the cause of death and sign the death certificates. Somehow, Delores finished this terrible time and walked the father and grandma out of the small family room that will remain in my memory as The Death Room, a place of loss and grief.

During the time spent with those children, other patients have streamed into the ER. The Triage Nurse, who was not directly involved as part of the resuscitation team, had been trying to control the flow of new patients. She had been courteously explaining that it will be a few more minutes before the ER doctor can see them. Most people understood and calmly waited, but I heard a few loud and demanding shouts.

"Where the hell is that damn doctor, on coffee break?!" and, "What kinda place is this, that I gotta wait so long?" and, the perennial, "Who I gotta complain to about this place?"

I can't help overhearing these "impatients" in the ER waiting room. Their pettiness angered me. I tried to get control of my feelings after talking with the children's daddy and grandma and had little concern about the sense of entitlement those people had who were shouting at the triage nurse.

I had another duty to attend to. I had to give a report and speak with the police who have arrived in the ER. I saw my friend, Chuck, who was a homicide detective, and walked over to him. Chuck had been to the children's home and told me more sad news, "We have the mother in custody. She admitted to giving both little boys an overdose of cough syrup and antihistamine before tucking them in bed last night. She called 911 this morning when she found them dead in their beds. The father had served her with divorce papers yesterday."

Chuck and I stood in the ER, shaking our heads at this evil.

Many years have passed since that day and I still cannot fathom the conflict and desperation that would drive a mother to deliberately kill her two young children. I remember following the trial in the local newspaper. The mother's plea of insanity was denied, and she was convicted of voluntary manslaughter.

Nurse Jean quit working in the ER shortly afterwards. Nurse

Delores transferred from the ER to the newborn nursery, where she could see new life every day.

And I kept soldiering on in the ER, hoping that I would recover emotional balance and continue to offer care and some comfort to the patients, but it became clear to me that I needed a change. The years of physical and emotional stress brought me to burnout.

Nowadays the emotional issues facing returning combat vets are well known, the post-traumatic stress syndrome or PTSD. Burnout in emergency workers, ER docs, ER nurses, and paramedics is similar. The work, which was once a challenge and source of purpose, now caused sleeplessness, anxiety, mood swings, and anger. The only effective treatment is avoidance.

I felt those feelings and left full time ER work in the trauma center. My wife and I bought an RV and travelled, far away from the ER. I was too young to totally quit working, but what could I do?

Chapter 23
Locum Tenens

"**M**ommy I hurts," the two-year old girl pointed to her chest.

Her young mother had brought little Daisy to the ER directly from her pediatrician's office across the street. She had told the triage nurse that her daughter has a rapid heartbeat. The nurse had applied the little stick-on electrodes to the girl's chest and called me over to look at the heart rhythm.

Daisy's heart raced at 240 beats per minute. That heart rate would cause an adult's blood pressure to plummet, leaving scant circulation in the vital coronary arteries that feed the heart with oxygen, causing cardiac arrest. But Daisy was in no danger of a heart attack. She had paroxysmal supraventricular tachycardia, PSVT. The upper chambers of her heart, the atria, had an abnormal group of pacemaker cells that were runaway, out of normal control. Unpredictably, these cells fired electrical impulses that overrode the normal pacemaker cells and caused very rapid heart rate, tachycardia.

I instructed the ER nurse to start an IV in Daisy's small arm vein. The child looked at us with big eyes but didn't flinch at the small sting of the needle insertion. Daisy's mom held the child on her lap, calming her, as I drew up the drug Adenosine into a small syringe.

"Daisy, this may sting a little for a second," I said to my little patient, as I pushed the drug into her vein rapidly. The nurse handed me another syringe filled with saline that I next pushed into the vein as a "chaser." The chase flushed the Adenosine directly into the central circulation and to Daisy's heart.

Her mom held her tight as Daisy cried out in pain from the intravenous Adenosine injection, a drug that stays in circulation for fifteen seconds. The cardiac monitor attached to my little patient showed a few rapid beats and sudden conversion to a normal heart rate of seventy beats per minute. That momentary pain passed and she looked up to her mommy and asked, "We go home now?"

I removed the IV and put a circus elephant Band-Aid on Daisy's arm. She looked at the tiny colorful scene and smiled. She was now pain free and her heart rate was normal.

I explained to Daisy's mom about the rapid heartbeat, an arrhythmia with the tongue-twister name: paroxysmal supraventricular tachycardia or PSVT, and she nodded.

"Yes, doctor, I know about PSVT. I've had it before. They had to shock me to stop it and I have a cardiologist who takes care of me."

I gave little Daisy a coloring book and crayons to occupy her while I watched her cardiac monitor for a few more minutes. She was happy and playful when mommy took her home. I felt a sense of accomplishment in the thirty minutes of taking care of this emergency, a feeling I had been missing for too long.

I had retired from the constant stress of the Trauma Center and was now doing *locum tenens* in small ERs in Virginia and North Carolina, where I held medical licenses. Locum tenens is a fancy Latin phrase roughly translated as "To Hold the Place." It means to fill in for a physician who is away from the practice, like a substitute teacher fills in for a full-timer. It was a new adventure for me, learning to work with unfamiliar nurses and doctors in different hospitals. I learned several electronic medical record systems as well, as no two hospitals used the same computer software for charting ER patient encounters.

Another part of the adventure was driving to some of these hospital assignments by RV. Liz and I enjoyed RV travel and found many beautiful campgrounds to set up a home-away-from-home. We especially loved the state parks with spacious campsites and lovely forests.

I had contracted with several national Locum Tenens firms who offered me positions at hospitals that had hired those firms to find coverage in their ER. These relationships permitted me to call the shots. If an assignment was not attractive, I turned it down. If a hospital ER had a reputation for poor medical care, I would not work there. And, if the hospital had misrepresented the job offer, by adding addition duties when I got to the site, I would report that to the contracting firm. One hospital changed the offer just before I arrived and informed me that I would have to write orders and be medically responsible for admitted patients, as well as all the patients in the ER. I did work one shift and refused others, as this new arrangement was a recipe for disaster. That hospital was saving money by risking the patient's well-being.

Most hospitals I did locums in were well run, smaller hospitals. I found the ER nurses and other physicians to be competent and compassionate, a joy to work with. I was less stressed and felt energized. I felt the same eagerness to go to work that I had had at the very beginning of my ER career.

Chapter 24
The Bear

Some ER doctors quit working in "the pit." That is what we call the Trauma Center to ourselves. The abnormal work schedules, the increasing volumes of paperwork, the stress of lawsuit threats, and the constant demands to be everything to everybody all the time, wear doctors down. I felt emotionally in the bottom of a hole with steep sides I could not climb out of. Many highly trained and experienced emergency physicians chose to work in other, much less stressful jobs.

I was no different and left full-time work in the trauma centers for a new phase in my ER career, doing part time work or locum tenens as I explained in the last chapter. Doing "locums," I saw how many different hospital's emergency departments functioned. I also met some of the most inspiring people who staffed these ERs. Working side-by-side with them reaffirmed my decision to leave the busy, sometimes overwhelming, urban trauma centers.

My new assignments were to work in more rural ERs. The work schedules, the hours, and the paperwork concerns were less stressful in the country than in the city, but I had a lot of new things to learn about my colleagues and how things got done.

My shifts at a rural North Carolina ER were pleasant, with the staff welcoming me warmly. Most of the patients streaming into the small seven bed emergency department had ambulatory complaints, not true emergencies. In medically underserved rural America, the ER is the safety net for the entire community, welcoming in people who had nowhere else to turn for help.

For the first time in many years I could talk to patients leisurely, without being rude and running to put out the next fire in a busy ER. I also worked with staff who knew the patients well, some of whom were neighbors or high school classmates. And I got to know the ER nursing staff, too.

I worked several day-shifts with Nurse Larry, and I noticed that he had a bit of a halt in his step when he got up from the nurse's station desk to see a patient. I asked him if his leg was tired. I had heard from the other ER nurses that he had had a road accident a few months ago.

"Doc, I feel much better. I was discharged from outpatient rehab this week. I showed them that I could go up and down stairs carrying weights. I also ran a few feet, turned around and ran back to the attendant. He said that I was good to go!" Larry said.

Larry had had to demonstrate strength and agility to keep his ER RN job after his accident.

He and I had spoken about his career change in mid-life before. Larry was over forty and had worked over fifteen years at the local Volvo diesel engine plant, where he had achieved certification as master diesel engine mechanic. He was promoted to lead mechanic, then shift supervisor, given big bonuses each year and was selected to go the Volvo truck engineering design center in Sweden for a year. Everything was pointing straight up in his career, but Larry felt unfulfilled. His family sensed it and, with a great deal of soul-searching, agreed with his plan. He knew that he wanted to help people, not just diesel engines, for his life's purpose.

He quit his job at Volvo, cashed in his pension, sold his truck, and started school again. Larry found a community college that would accept him into the practical nurse program. For the next two years, and a lot of his savings, he learned all he could. He graduated with straight A's. One of his professors called the University and recommended him. At the University, he was accepted into the eighteen-month registered nurse program. He laughed when he told me that he was old enough to be the father of his classmates. Larry's wife worked two jobs, at the Piggly Wiggly and at a Dollar General. Their fourteen-year-old son got a paper route to help, too. Larry told me this with pride in his family and with a bit of a tear in his eyes. He wiped his face to hide this, "Damn allergies are acting up again," he said.

Larry graduated at the top of his nursing school class, and passed the registry exam. He had become a Registered Nurse at the age of forty-two.

The hospital was happy to hire him. He worked two years on the wards, including OB and the ICU, where he found a calling in acute care and applied for his dream job, the ER.

He had just started working in the ER, commuting from the family's double-wide trailer home to the hospital at 6 AM, for his dayshift. He had been riding a motorcycle for years, having bought a used bike when he sold his truck for school money, so he was an experienced operator.

"I'd been riding that road for many years and never saw anything like it before. I had to make a split-second decision, it was life or death, Doc," Larry said.

The Bear

In the middle of the road, directly in front of his moving motorcycle, was a black bear. Black bears in North Carolina can weigh four hundred pounds or more. Running into a bear with a truck is very dangerous for the driver; running into a bear riding a motorcycle is lethal for the rider.

"I knew I would be killed if I hit the bear, so I turned the bike hard, lost traction and flew off the motorcycle, onto the side of the blacktop. The bike skidded with a loud sound, startling the bear, who lit out for the tree line, away from me lying on the ground," Larry said.

"I was stunned, covered in dirt, flat on my back. I heard my bike ticking over as the engine cooled, then no sounds. I think I heard a few crows arguing, but that was all. It was too early for this rural road to have any traffic or farm equipment. I took this road to work every day and knew I was alone," he continued.

"I puked with the pain in my legs when I tried to push down on the dirt to sit up. I got my helmet off and saw blood on my palms, but my legs looked straight when I looked down. I figured that I got some road rash and a wrecked bike, that's it," Larry said.

He told me that he wasn't sure how long he lay on the roadside; his watch and band had been torn off his wrist. He remembered hoping some farmer would see him and stop. He also worried that the farmer would not see him and run over him with a tractor.

"Doc, I was scared. I tried to crawl, but any big movement caused agony. Even just trying to shift myself made me nauseated with the pain. I calmed down by taking some deep breaths and thinking about my family. I sure as hell was not gonna die!"

—⋀—

He found his cell phone in the pocket of his leather riding jacket. It wasn't even scratched. He had a strong signal and called 911.

It took the local rescue squad twenty minutes to find him. They had been cruising all the rural roads until they spotted the crumpled motorcycle on the side of the road.

They drove Larry to the University Trauma Center where the surgeons found both his legs were broken. Larry recounted that he had several surgeries including a titanium rod in one leg and pins in the other leg.

"They were great. The surgeons did a lot for me. They promised me that I'd walk again. I guess it didn't hurt that my classmates were part of the nursing team," he said with some embarrassment and pride in his voice.

Larry stood up and walked with a slight limp to the nurse triage desk, he smiled at the patient and took the vital signs. He put the thermometer under the patient's tongue, recording the temperature, applied the Velcro edged blood pressure cuff, puffed it up as he listened with his stethoscope over the elbow artery. He counted the patient's breaths with his watch and recorded all these things on the chart.

I marveled at the dedication and sacrifice he had made just to learn to take those vital signs, to help another human being. Larry, a nurse called to compassion and caring, trading in his diesel truck wrench for a stethoscope, inspired me.

The EMS truck pulled into the ambulance bay and a paramedic came to the nurse's station, leaned over and asked for some assistance. Larry got up and rolled the ER wheelchair through the automatic doors out to the back of the unit. He then rolled the patient back into Room 2, our small trauma room.

The patient was a big man, bearded with his hair pulled back into a pony tail. He wore a Harley-Davidson motorcycle jacket with black jeans and was seated in the wheelchair in pain. Larry was removing the left boot with some difficulty. The patient braced his big arms on the armrests and grimaced as the boot came off, revealing a swollen ankle.

"That damn kick stand on my bike broke and the bike fell over onto my foot when I got off! Had to get my pals to lift it off my left leg. It really throbbed when I tried to walk, so they called 911 for me."

I felt good pulses in his injured ankle and gave him pain medicine before getting x-rays of his left ankle and left foot. I didn't feel dislocations or instability of his left foot or ankle, which was a good sign, since crush injuries can be severe, even limb and life threatening.

The x-ray showed a non-displaced fracture of his left ankle. Larry and I applied a plaster splint to his ankle and showed him how to walk with crutches. I prescribed pain pills and gave him a referral to the orthopedist for follow- up care.

As I was writing up the chart I overheard Larry and the patient conversing. I couldn't hear all of it, but I did hear what Larry said to his fellow injured motorcyclist.

"Yeah, it's true, motorcycles are unsafe at any speed!"

Both of them laughed, I though a bit ruefully, considering that one got hurt flying off and one got hurt just standing next to a motorcycle.

Chapter 25
Misdiagnosis

"**S**he's been coughing and wheezing all night," the mother of my fourteen-year-old patient told me. Mom had taken her teenaged daughter to the pediatrician that morning for the cough. His prescribed medicine was not stopping Claudia's cough.

It was October in Eastern Virginia, the cough and cold season. I had seen many people with runny noses, coughing and wheezing all day long. It was past 7 PM, the end of my dayshift, and I had turned over the responsibility of a few dayshift patients to the oncoming night shift ER doc. I knew how it felt to pick up patients from another doctor at change of shift and wanted to see a few "quickie" cases to lighten the burden. A "quickie" case usually was a young patient with a simple laceration to repair or a trivial complaint, like a cough from an upper respiratory viral infection, a cold.

I picked up the ER chart and noted that the girl did not have a fever, but was breathing twenty-five times a minute, a bit abnormal. In appearance, she was healthy with clear skin and I heard some wheezing in her lungs. Mom confirmed that she had had asthma as a youngster but was not taking any medicines for wheezing now.

I ordered respiratory therapy to give her inhaled bronchodilators and the girl improved. It was my usual practice to get a chest x-ray after treatment of wheezing, as I had seen

157

pneumonia masquerade as asthma before, but didn't see any of the tell-tale shadows of lung infection on the films.

Claudia had stopped coughing and wanted to go home. I confirmed with her mother that she was taking the pediatrician's medicine as prescribed and asked her to continue with it. I told Claudia and her mom that the chest x-ray did not show pneumonia and I asked them to return to the ER if she started coughing again.

This patient was seen in 1989 and it was accepted practice for x-rays read by the doctor on duty in the ER to be read again by the radiologist to ensure accuracy. But, depending on the radiologist "reader," a week might go by before the typed report was sent to the emergency department. There was no formal follow-up on these x-ray reports sent to the ER and I just happened to see that chest x-ray report several days after I had treated that fourteen-year-old girl. The radiologist thought that the patient's heart was enlarged. The heart shadow on the normal chest x-ray does change shape with respiration. The normal heart is a bit larger with inhalation and a bit smaller with exhalation, but I now saw that the girl's heart was bigger than it should be. I had mistaken the heart shadow and size as normal. I was concentrating on the wheezing sounds, looking for and not finding pneumonia.

Two months later, I heard from a colleague at the Norfolk Children's Hospital that the girl had been transferred to his center with severe heart failure. Every medical treatment failed and she had to have a heart transplant. Claudia's heart had been severely damaged by a virus.

Had I missed the early stage of viral myocarditis? I thought that the process of heart damage must have started when I had treated Claudia for wheezing, that one ER visit. Her chest x-ray had shown the totally unexpected finding of an enlarged heart, and I missed it. I misdiagnosed Claudia, calling her failing heart a case of asthma.

I had made the most common error in ER diagnosis. This error is now called Availability. It means the doctor has in mind an "available" convenient pattern: 1) fall epidemic of upper respiratory illnesses, 2) young, healthy girl seen that day by her pediatrician, 3) wheezing that improved with inhaler bronchodilator asthma medicine = *asthma attack*. Pattern recognition, a most useful skill in any diagnostician's toolbox is essential. It is a necessary skill in the ER, but not always a sufficient skill to figure out what is the cause of the patient's distress. I had not seen that Claudia's wheezing was caused by her failing heart.

Most ER doctors solve the mystery of the patient's illness by forming a differential diagnosis in mind, a mental laundry list of anything that could cause a patient's symptoms. In the busy ER, this list is usually short and concise. No reasonable person expects the soup-to-nuts work-up with multiple consultants and extensive testing in a short ER visit. The ER motto is: "Ready! Shoot! Aim!" which means the patient must be treated first, while the evaluation proceeds simultaneously, sometimes it is a formula for error.

There is a brighter future in emergency medicine as the study of decision analysis, studying how mistakes are made, comes up with solutions to make patient care safer and quicker. The first steps have been taken to relieve some of the pressure on the decision maker in the ER. Those positive changes include shortening the length of shifts, increasing the number of doctors, trained physician assistants, and nurse practitioners on duty at one time, and having more trained radiologists specializing in emergency medicine procedures. The implementation of computerized emergency charting as well as x-ray and computed tomography results are read immediately by the radiologist and reported directly to the ER physician's computer terminal, as well as direct phone call. Any changes in the radiologist's reading of any discrepancies are transmitted to the ER electronically and printed for timely review, closing the information loop every time.

The most important change is a subtle one in the emergency physician. With the expanding knowledge about decision mistakes, whether it is the disaster of the BP oil spill in the Gulf of Mexico, The Three Mile Island nuclear power plant melt down, or the Chernobyl radiation contamination, much has been learned about how human beings decide. The ER has become a laboratory for the study of metacognition, a big word that means thinking about the thought process.

I questioned myself about the pattern of my decision making. Was I putting too much weight on the patient's lab tests, the demeanor of the patient, his medical complaint? Had I adequately answered each question the patient had raised? Was I in a hurry? Was there something about the patient I had a bias or prejudice about? Was I too emotionally involved? Was I too remote, too abrupt?

I knew it was more likely to make errors of judgment when exhausted and overwhelmed with patients, the number of decisions not allowing reflection. In that setting, pattern recognition is vital for safely caring patients in a chaotic ER. In those very busy times recognizing patterns of illness and injury can be life-saving.

The pattern of a young woman with shortness of breath was indelibly burned into my memory. Could I have done more for fourteen-year-old Claudia in the ER all those years ago? I was not going to forget her or my error. These thoughts came to mind as I worked as a *locums* at a small rural hospital in Virginia.

"I went to my OB yesterday and I still feel bad. I told them I didn't feel good after the baby. They told me it was just post-partum depression and gave me some pills," she said.

Mrs. Lacy King was a thirty-six-year-old lady who was two months' post-partum, angry, and concerned. I let her finish without interruption.

"She is my fourth baby and I never felt like this after the others," she added. "The office just blew me off, I didn't even see the OB, just the midwife."

She had had a normal pregnancy and vaginal delivery. There was no diabetes, high blood pressure, or urinary tract infections. The records she brought showed that she had not had excessive weight gain, never smoked, drank alcohol, or used illicit drugs, just the prenatal vitamins recommended by her doctor. Everything looked pretty routine with a happy healthy baby as the outcome. But Mrs. King still felt bad.

I asked her some general questions, not seeing much in her obstetrical record to explain her symptoms. I cast the net widely, hoping to catch any small clues. Yes, she did have a good appetite with no nausea, vomiting, or diarrhea. She denied blood in her urine or stinging when passing water. She admitted of some mild ankle swelling but denied leg pain or trouble walking.

My last question triggered an important response.

"Doctor, I don't have trouble walking, I just have to stop and catch my breath a lot," she replied. "The office said it was normal for women after childbirth to be sore and not want to walk, but this is different. They wouldn't listen to me."

I recognized that the OB office had concluded that this patient fit their pattern of post-partum depression. Could they have made a common "availability" mistake, like mine?

I worried about what her symptoms could mean for this mother; they were not post-partum depression, of that I was certain.

She had trouble sleeping, not because she had emotional problems. She needed to raise her head on two pillows just to fall asleep. When she said, "two pillows," my ears stood up. "Two Pillows" to sleep on, is in medical lingo, *orthopnea*. It means being short of breath when you are flat on your back. It is a symptom of severe cardiac dysfunction. Heart failure of sudden onset, in her case, two months after normal childbirth suggested a diagnosis to me. I had missed early heart failure in young Claudia many years ago, and there were alarming similarities to Mrs. King's symptoms. Could these two women, one a young teenager, the other a young middle-ager have the same disease?

Mrs. King's EKG, usually a helpful clue, was abnormal, but not diagnostic. Her chest x-ray showed an enlarged heart and the cloudy lung shadows which meant her lungs were filling up with fluid her heart could no longer pump out.

This was post-partum myocarditis. A virus had damaged Mrs. King's heart, just as a virus had destroyed young Claudia's. Mrs. King was unable to sleep normally and got short of breath with

Life in the Balance

slight exertion, because her damaged heart could not clear fluid from her lungs any longer.

I explained my diagnosis to Mrs. King. She was very quiet and nodded her head in agreement. "I told them I felt bad, and they didn't have a clue!"

I called the cardiology service at Medical College of Virginia in Richmond. They accepted her and sent the transport helicopter to the small rural hospital.

I did not have another shift at this hospital for several weeks. I was working at other facilities in the meantime and wanted to get some follow up on Mrs. King.

I called the cardiac service at MCV. The resident who took care of Mrs. King read some of her chart and filled me in on some details. Mrs. King went from the helicopter directly to the cardiac lab in the University hospital. She gave permission for a cardiac catheterization that night. He read some of the results which showed normal coronary arteries. The pressures inside the cardiac chambers were abnormally high and a heart muscle biopsy was sent to pathology. The biopsy showed destruction of muscle cells and other findings characteristic of viral infection.

The cardiology resident said he had cared for her after the catheterization. Her heart failure improved with medicine and she went home. He told me she had returned to the clinic with her baby girl and he had to tell Mrs. King that she would need a heart transplant soon.

After speaking with the cardiology resident, I reflected that I made the correct diagnosis for Mrs. King and that my misdiagnosis of Claudia stayed with me, helping me to get it right for another patient.

I deliberately had not called Mrs. King's OB's office when she came directly from there to the ER. Contact with them might have led me into another serious thought error. The "confirmation error" happens when a patient is referred for a second opinion, or more frequently, like this lady, goes to the ER.

It can be a difficult process to discount a previous doctor's work-up. The medical profession tends to protect its own, and poorly spoken criticism of another's work is discouraged. The doctor who disrespects or badmouths another's work is just as vilified as the turncoat doctors-for-hire who travel the country as well-paid experts in medical malpractice trials. It is much more comfortable to be generous in giving that second opinion if, in honesty, it confirms the original diagnosis. It doesn't help the patient to think less of the first attending physician; it can erode the patient's confidence needed for compliance to reasonable therapy. But, just automatically accepting what has already been done for the patient is not perfect, either.

Mrs. King, angry at her OB when she came to the ER, felt that she had not been listened to or appreciated by the office staff at that visit. She had a serious heart problem that the OB office missed by dismissing her complaints without thoughtful inquiry. I could understand how it could happen in a busy office. I had made the same mistake in missing Claudia's heart failure, years ago.

Mrs. King had the correct diagnosis because I had made a misdiagnosis of Claudia, years ago.

Chapter 26
A Waste of Time

"**D**oc, I'm sorry to waste your time, you probably have some sick patients to see. She's really exaggerating. It's just a sinus condition, nothing more."

Mr. Jerome Sanders looked over at his wife sitting at the side of the ER stretcher and gave me the raised eyebrows and head nod in her direction, trying to enlist masculine disdain of "the little woman."

Mrs. Sanders was a well-dressed lady sitting with her knees together, arms wrapped around herself and gave me her own eye-roll in response to what her husband had just said to me. She began to say something but stopped herself.

"Mr. Sanders please take off your clothes and put on the examining gown," I requested.

I noticed that his shirt was not buttoned evenly, he had mismatched socks and he had missed several belt loops. His clothes were clean and neatly pressed. I did not see food or urine stains.

He was clumsy unbuttoning his shirt and swayed on his feet as he unbuckled his belt to take off his slacks. He saw me watching and leaned back against the stretcher to complete the task. He caught himself with his hand on the stretcher when he leaned over to take off his shoes and socks.

He slipped on the cotton examining gown easily and while he was standing, I asked him to stand on one leg, to check for balance. I had my arms on either side of him and he lurched to the side, laughing as I caught him.

"Never was good at gymnastics, Doc!" he said with a grin.

After he was seated on the stretcher I asked him to do rapid alternating movements with his hands, a test of coordination. I wanted him to alternatively slap his thighs with his palms, turn the hands over, and slap with the back of his hands. He couldn't keep the beat and again snorted to me, "This is silly, Doc!"

His blood pressure, breathing rate, heat-beat, and temperature were normal. There were no abnormal sounds in his carotid arteries when I put my stethoscope over each side of his neck, which meant he had no large blockages. The circulation in his brain seemed normal.

I tapped him with my arrow-shaped rubber reflex hammer on his right knee to test his patellar reflex and his foot shot up involuntarily, like he was kicking for a field goal. But when I tapped the left knee, the reflex leg movement was normal. These deep tendon reflexes normally are symmetrical. This abnormal, hyperactive right patellar reflex indicated a central nervous system problem, a stroke, elevated brain pressure, a neurodegenerative disorder, or a tumor.

I opened a safety pin, asked him to close his eyes and tell me when I touched him on his face and his palms with the pin. He had normal sensations. The sensory nerves send signals to the brain for touch, pain and temperature, pressure, and proprioception. The pin tested his sense of touch.

I asked Mr. Sanders to recline on the stretcher and, with his eyes closed, to tell me where I had moved his big toe. I moved the toe either upward, toward his head, or downward, away from his head. He was accurate each time, which indicated that his position sense was intact. This was an important clue that his neurological problem was probably caused by a clotted brain artery, a stroke.

"How's your vision and hearing?" I asked him

"Doc, I wear reading glasses that's all," he answered.

I had never treated him before, so I didn't know if these short answers were normal for him or a sign of intellectual decline. I asked him to remember three things, "Watch, Pen, Eyeglasses" for five minutes. After five minutes, he rattled off the three things, in order, without hesitation. He remembered the items when I quizzed him twenty minutes later, too. That memory retention performance helped me to rule out dementia.

"Have you had any trouble with urination or bowel movements?" I asked him.

"Doc, I get up at night to pee, that's all," he answered quickly.

I looked over to Mrs. Sanders. She was slowly shaking her head. She disagreed but had decided not to interrupt her husband.

I examined his cranial nerves. These nerves come directly out of the skull, the cranium. All the other nerves originate in the brain, but course out from the spinal cord, hence are called spinal nerves.

The twelve cranial nerves are matched pairs. They control sight and eye movements, and other vital functions. The auditory nerves allow hearing. The facial nerves control muscles in the face. The lingual cranial nerves are dedicated to control of the tongue. Sticking the tongue straight out of the mouth is normal, however, if the tongue is deviated to one side it indicates a serious condition. I examined Mr. Sanders and found these nerves to be normal. The optic nerve, which sends images to the visual cortex in the very back of the brain, is the only nerve that can be seen directly.

In the ER, unlike the eye doctor's office, dilating the patient's pupils with eye drops is rarely done. I would turn off the lights in the patient's room with the door closed to get the pupils to dilate normally in response to the dark, rather than use drops. After a few minutes in the dark, Mr. Sander's pupils were wider and I picked up my direct ophthalmoscope to examine his retina. His retinas had a bleached color, not the normal healthy pink. More ominously, the optic nerve heads, which normally form a cup where the nerve fibers come out and flower over the retina, were swollen, ballooning. His optic nerves were being pushed from behind. The pressure in his brain was too high, squeezing the tiny blood vessels in his retinas, blanching them, threating him with blindness.

I turned the lights back on the examining room and Mrs.

Sanders stood up and spoke for the first time.

"Doctor, he pees in his pants every day and yesterday he didn't get to the bathroom in time. He soiled himself. And he's taking Tylenol every four hours for his headaches. I don't think this is sinusitis," she said.

He glared at her when she revealed this embarrassing truth.

I broke the silence. "We'll need to do a special head CT, using intravenous dye. Sir, do you have any allergies?"

Mr. Sanders shook his head, still starring at his wife, who, standing up, returned his gaze.

I worried that the scan might show a malignant brain tumor. The history and physical examination led me there. In my experience, patients give the history that helps to make the diagnosis. My medical school mentor often remarked that listening to the patient gave the clinician the answer. In Mr. Sander's case, it was not so. His replies to my questions were terse and uncommunicative because of his profound denial of disease.

Denial is a powerful force in all of us. Mr. Sanders and I are the same age and I felt his distress deeply. I identified with him as a person who had a shared history, but I wouldn't let that cloud my judgment. I had grown in the profession and had a detached concern for Mr. and Mrs. Sanders. I had sensitivity toward them as people and simultaneously maintained the professional distance needed to help them.

The contrast CT, where intravenous dye is injected before the computerized tomography x-rays are shot, showed a very vascular, malignant brain tumor in Mr. Sander's frontal brain lobes.

I returned to their examining room and told them both the results of the CT. They were stunned by this bad news, but calm. Mrs. Sanders asked me, "Doctor, what do we do now?"

I contacted the oncologist who would see them tomorrow in the office. I also arranged for a consultation with neurosurgery. I also administered strong steroid medicine and pain medicine to treat Mr. Sanders brain swelling and pain. The medicine gave relief and they went home.

Several days later I received a copy of the neurosurgeon's operative note. He had put in a shunt to reduce the brain pressure and had taken a brain tumor biopsy. The pathologist identified the cells as invasive glioblastoma, a rapidly lethal disease. The oncologist continued the medicines I had started in the ER, and started some chemotherapy that had just been approved for treatment. Mr. Sanders chose hospice for dignified end-of-life care, he did not want cardiopulmonary resuscitation and prolonged ventilator care.

In the beginning years of my emergency medicine career, most of the patients were young, victims of accident or trauma. Now, in my last years in the ER, as a locum tenens doctor, the patient demographics changed. Most of the patients now were much older, chronically ill, suffering from heart disease, cancer, senility, and complex infections. Ambulances now transported nursing home patients to the ER for urinary tract infections, colds, or infected bedsores. Most of these sick elderly patients were demented or confused, making the ER an annex, not a trauma center. Many had chosen hospice care, allowing only fluids and antibiotics if needed, but refusing the heroics of CPR and ventilator care. Some of the family members had denial issues and wanted "everything" to be done. The patient's written directive was followed as a matter of law, but tender feelings had to be respected during a crisis.

I saw Mr. Sanders again in the ER when he had severe abdominal pain and threw up blood.

"Doctor, I've been doing so well since you found the tumor. I still can climb stairs and walk every day. I've stopped crapping my pants, but now I'm puking blood."

I admitted him when a nasogastric tube showed continuous stomach bleeding. His blood count and blood pressure remained very low and he responded to conservative therapy in the hospital. The bleeding stopped, and the cause seemed to be the large dosage of steroids he had been taking to reduce brain swelling.

Mrs. Sanders reminded me that Mr. Sanders had signed an advance directive making her his power of attorney for health matters. He didn't want "heroics" to "prolong my death." She drove him home and took him for follow-up appointments with his oncologist who lowered the steroid dose the next day.

About a year later Mr. Sanders was brought to the ER in the middle of the night. He had a seizure and was comatose. One of my colleagues saw him, started anticonvulsants and did a lumbar puncture which showed a fungal meningitis infection.

I was surprised when I visited Mr. Sanders a few days later in the ICU. He was awake and cheerful, "Hey Doc, I'm that bad penny that keeps coming back!"

I sat at his bedside and he told me that they had changed his chemotherapy last week and he was sure it was a reaction to the new medicine. I told him that I was happy to see him again and excused myself to speak with Mrs. Sanders in the hallway.

"Doctor, I've called our children to come to the hospital to see him one last time. The oncologist told him that there were no other medicines to try and the tumor is getting bigger."

A day later I learned that Mr. Sanders saw his children at his bedside and shortly after they said their goodbyes, he died in the ICU. The fungal meningitis was listed as the cause of death in a patient on chemotherapy for glioblastoma.

He had died of the brain tumor, but had lived well, keeping his sense of humor and love of his family to the very end.

Chapter 27

A Man Bitten in the Eye by a Bug

It was a beautiful summer Saturday in North Carolina, sunny and warm as I went to work my *locums* shift in a small, rural hospital. My shifts had been boring, with only various outpatient illnesses seen and treated. The few doctor's offices in the community were full all the time and patients used the local ER as a drop-in clinic when they were unable to get a regular appointment. The nurses, bored with the weekend routine, had their feet up and were reading magazines at their stations. The time on the clock over their heads seemed to have slowed to a crawl. Then I saw a nurse, head nodding, drop her magazine to the floor when the radio claxon startled her awake. The paramedics called, "We've got a forty-five-year-old man, conscious, bit in the eye by a bug!"

I hadn't worked with this local EMS and didn't know how good they were. My experience with rural emergency medical systems at other locum assignments had been spotty. Some were very professional, and others were starting out, learning how to be emergency first responders. Most of the young people on the rescue squads were volunteers, high school graduates with a passion for serving others. I respected their motivation and dedication very much but had doubts about their judgments in the field. Additionally, I had concerns about the abilities of the nurses in this ER. The few shifts I had worked here had not been challenging and I wondered how they would perform in a crunch. Taking their cue from the EMS call, they moved in slow motion to set up for a severe allergic reaction of some kind. I was worried that the EMS rookies had not called to confirm that they had administered shots of steroids or epinephrine to a patient with what could be an allergic emergency. The EMS ambulance was driving to this ER from about twenty miles away, near Jordan Lake and those shots could be life-saving.

The voice on the radio was frantic, "He's unconscious now!"

I heard the stress in that radio voice, asked for the patient's vital signs and heard nothing but static. The ambulance was moving and they had left the mike open. If they had taken the vital signs, I couldn't hear them. It sounded like a panic situation in the back of the rescue truck, with loud shouts and metal clattering.

A few minutes later, I heard the diesel engine as the ambulance pulled into the ER bay and the back doors of the truck slammed open. I saw four young rescuers rolling a stretcher as fast as they could to the trauma bay, sweat pouring off their faces.

The man on their stretcher was barefoot, wearing a red tee shirt with a football logo and a dark colored bathing suit, dripping water. He did not have hives on his face or skin. He didn't respond to my questions or touch, as we moved him from the EMS stretcher to the ER stretcher. I felt a fast pulse in his right wrist and the nurses announced that his blood pressure was elevated. He had a large left pupil that did not react when I shined my bright penlight. His right pupil constricted immediately when the light beamed into it.

He was breathing deeply but did not move when I pinched the skin in the web between his right thumb and index finger. This failure to withdraw from a painful stimulus meant that he was comatose, his brain was shutting down.

This was no bug bite allergy, it was something causing brain swelling and pushing down on his brain stem. The third cranial nerves live in the brain stem. The third nerve on the right controls the right pupil, the third nerve on the left side controls the left pupil. This patient had something increasing the pressure in his brain, pushing on his left third cranial nerve, paralyzing the left pupil wide open. The brain stem also controls heartbeat and respiration. Continued pressure on the brain stem stops the heart and breathing. If I can't stop the pressure crushing his brain stem, he would be dead in the next three minutes or less.

The rescue squad had started an IV and I administered mannitol, a drug that pulled excess water out of the swollen brain and relieved some of the squeezing on the brain stem. The nurses passed a Foley catheter into the patient's urinary bladder at the same time. Mannitol made him pee a lot.

This comatose patient was at risk for vomiting and choking to death. To prevent that choking from killing him, I was faced with a dilemma. Anesthesiologists passed an endotracheal tube for that very reason, in a patient going for an operation. In a comatose patient, passing an endotracheal tube in that standard manner is lethal. There is a reflex reaction in comatose patients.

It is hard wired into our brains. When we are awake, we gag and puke if you put a tube in our mouths and down our throats. When we are comatose, a primitive reflex rockets our heart rate and blood pressure if you just simply pushed a tube down our throat into our windpipe. That kind of blood pressure elevation would rapidly increase pressure on the brain stem, stopping our heart and breathing.

I used the training I had learned at an Advanced Airway Management Course in Toronto, Canada to blunt that deadly reflex in my comatose patient. The first step, put that reflex to sleep with intravenous Lidocaine, a drug that anesthetizes nerves. The second step, administer the sedative Etomidate. It is the best drug for that purpose, as it does not affect the heart rate or blood pressure. The third step, administer Fentanyl, a powerful narcotic painkiller thirty to forty times more powerful than Morphine. Pain signals in the comatose patient can make brain swelling worse, so it is important to block pain. Finally, I pushed Succinylcholine, a fast-acting, short-lived drug, derived from the poison Amazon Indians used to blow dart prey, into the vein quickly.

I waited for the paralysis of his muscles to be complete, then passed the endotracheal tube into his mouth, down to his trachea. I injected ten milliliters of sterile saline into the balloon at the tip of the endotracheal tube, sealing and protecting the patient from choking on vomit. The nurses attached the football shaped Ambu bag to the endotracheal tube and began squeezing it, pushing oxygen into his lungs.

The ER nurses and I pushed his stretcher to the Radiology

department for a head C.T. The Computed Tomography x-ray of a patient 's head was the quickest and most accurate method to find out the cause of my patient's coma.

The patient placed into the cylindrical C.T. and the technician started the scan. The big machine makes a loud, mechanical sound, like a freight train, as his brain was scanned. I barely heard the clatter, because I focused on the patient whose life I held in my hands.

The nurses pulled him from the machine and I walked to the technician's console where the head C.T. images began to arrive at his video screen. I immediately saw the problem. This "bug bite" was a huge blood clot on the brain, an epidural hematoma. It is one of the most deadly strokes a person can endure, and fatal if not removed.

I had paralyzed the patient's muscles with drugs and now I felt paralyzed under the weight of decision making. This little hospital had no capacity to treat an expanding bleeding in the brain. It had been forty minutes since the beginning of his brain bleeding and time was running out. The intravenous Mannitol had reduced some of the swelling, but not the bleeding, which continued. I estimated that the positive effect of the Mannitol was almost completed.

I called Duke University Medical Center and spoke with a neurosurgeon. He would send the helicopter to our hospital and take the patient to the operating room immediately.

I added more Mannitol to his intravenous fluids and gave him Pavulon, a longer-acting muscle paralyzer, so the patient won't fight the ventilator used in flight to Duke Medical Center. I thanked God that it was a bright, clear day, perfect flying weather for the emergency helicopter, which landed on the hospital helipad within twelve minutes of my call to the neurosurgeon. The nurses and I rushed the stretcher out of the ER, down the path to the waiting flight nurse. We loaded the patient into the helicopter through its open back doors and closed them. The flight nurse waved to us as the helicopter lifted off, elapsed time, three minutes.

A few minutes after the helicopter flew away, the nurse told me that the patient's wife and children had arrived in the ER.

The nurses and I walked them to the family room. The wife was barely holding it together. A boy about nine, held his younger sister's hand and looked back and forth between his mom and the nurses. He knew something bad had happened, but he protected the little girl. She was sucking her thumb and looked up at us with big eyes and dried tears on her cheeks.

I introduced myself and asked them to sit down with me. His wife told me that they were boating on the lake when her husband shouted, "Something just flew into my eye and I'm blind!"

"He fell down and the children started screaming. The boat was still running and I had to stop it to call 911. I drove the boat to the landing and the rescue men carried him out of the boat to the ambulance." She caught her breath, then continued. "Some men at the dock got the boat tied up and told me where the hospital was."

I sat with her and the children and explained that he had

suffered a stroke caused by bleeding. I explained that the helicopter took him to Duke University Medical Center for emergency brain surgery. She was speechless but nodded in understanding. Her children held her hands as she stood up with them.

The ER nurses had a prepared handout to give her to find neurosurgery at Duke. They had a map to help her with the fastest route. The nurses were compassionate and took time to answer her questions and explain the route in detail. She paid close attention and I could see that she was controlling her fears for her young children.

I knew she and the children were stunned and shocked by all that had happened suddenly. Just an hour ago the family was on their boat for a fun day on Jordan Lake, and now this. I asked her if she felt OK to drive and she looked at me and nodded. The nurses helped her and the children into the car and gave her all the phone numbers to call at Duke.

I walked them out to their car and watched her drive away. I marveled at her presence of mind and courage. Her quick thinking saved his life. Could any of us act with such composure and decisiveness in a crisis? She was a rare and precious heroine to me.

Practicing emergency medicine had allowed me to see the worst in people much of the time. It also allowed me to see the very best in people, too. It was a privilege to be part of these lives.

Three days later I got a phone call from Duke. My patient had survived emergency brain surgery with removal of the blood clot. He had been extubated and was breathing on his own, in the Surgical Intensive Care Unit and soon to discharged. I was glad to hear that I had enough time to save his life, but worried about what that life might offer after a stroke. I always worried about the lasting damage from brain injury, especially from trauma or gunshot wounds.

Little more than a month later the ER nurses called me over to see the flowers. The note accompanying them said, "Paul has returned to work and feels fine. May God bless you all." It was signed by his wife. Just below her name, in childish crayon, "thank you nurse and docter, XO XO Billy & Lisa"

Chapter 28
Erin's Smoke Break

The night shift at Martin General Hospital had been non-stop. After the last admitted patient was tucked in upstairs at 4 AM, it was a good time for a coffee break. The shift had started at 7 PM with several patients injured in a car accident brought in by rescue squad. With the night shift nurses, Kenny and Erin, we had been hustling ever since, treating many patients with lacerations, heart attacks, pneumonia, and the flu.

The ER was finally quiet, and I got a coffee from the break room, walked back to my desk and sat on the swivel chair in the nurse's station. Kenny and Erin each took turns going outside the ER to the ambulance bay for a smoke. Several years later Martin General would become a smoke-free campus, but before then this North Carolina hospital looked the other way. After all, as we all joked, here in tobacco growing country, "It's a felony not to smoke!"

Erin returned from the ambulance bay and sat down at the nurse's station counter, a few feet from me. I was typing on the emergency medical record computer, catching up on the chart work I had put off while treating the patients. My back was turned away from her as I heard her sigh. I spun around on my chair and saw her resting her head on the counter, breathing deeply.

I noted a problem on my charts and asked her, "Erin, help me remember the last drug we gave that lady we just admitted."

Erin didn't answer me, and I gave her shoulder a gentle shake. She began to slide off her chair and I caught her before she hit the floor. Her face was slack and her eyes were rolled back into her head. I grabbed both of her shoulders and shook them hard. Her head lolled like a rag doll, but she made no response. Erin was unconscious. I shouted, "Kenny, help!"

He and I lifted Erin and rushed her to a stretcher. Kenny pulled her tunic top apart and applied the cardiac leads to her chest. I pressed the cardiac paddles to her chest for a quick look at the heart monitor mounted on the wall. Her heart was beating two hundred fifty times a minute, way too fast to maintain blood pressure. I was worried that she may have suffered a stroke from the low blood pressure. Maybe Erin has had a seizure, or a heart attack. A few minutes earlier I was tired, hoping for the shift to end quietly, and now this!

Kenny got an IV running in Erin's arm and I tried the Valsalva maneuver to slow the heart rate. The Valsalva maneuver included rubbing the side of the neck, stimulating the patient's carotid artery reflex. It was a very old, beside trick I had learned when I first treated rapid heart rate. Erin's heart did slow down then rocketed up again. Kenny pushed two doses of Adenosine into the IV while I held the cardiac paddles and pushed the charge button on the cardiac defibrillator. This was a new model and charged up within fifteen seconds. If the Adenosine didn't interrupt this arrhythmia soon, I had to shock her to stop this life-threatening rapid heart rate.

Kenny and I concentrated on the heart monitor above Erin's stretcher. I hoped that I would not have to shock her with the paddles. I knew that the electricity would stop her heart, giving her normal cardiac pacemaker cells a chance to restart in a normal rhythm and heart rate. I also dreaded doing that since, rarely, the patient's heart didn't restart.

The cardiac monitor showed her heart had stopped for a few seconds after the Adenosine and then restarted in the normal rhythm. Erin came back to the world and looked up at Kenny holding an empty syringe and then at me, with the charged cardiac paddles poised over her chest. She sat up quickly and said, "What happened? What's going on?"

Erin saw the stick-on cardiac monitor pads on her chest and looked up at the cardiac monitor. I showed her the paper print-out from the monitor. It showed a very rapid heart rate with the characteristics of atrial tachycardia. The normal pacemaker cells live in the atria, the top chambers of the heart. When there is an abnormal pathway, a short circuit around the normal cells, the atria run wild and send that fast signal to the lower heart chambers, the ventricles. A heart rate of two hundred fifty beats a minute did not allow the ventricles to pump out enough blood to keep a person conscious, and that extremely fast rate would not allow blood to circulate through the coronary arteries, starving the heart muscles of oxygen as they contracted. Atrial tachycardia in young patients, like Erin, didn't cause permanent heart damage. In older patients, with blockages in the coronary arteries, the very rapid heart rate can be fatal.

Kenny and I were relieved to see that Erin was back to her usual state of mind. She had a life-threatening arrhythmia in the right place at the right time.

I started her on pills to prevent the atrial tachycardia and recommended she see a cardiologist as soon as possible. I also recommended she stop smoking. She and Kenny shared a look and I knew I was wasting my breath on these life-long cigarette smokers.

Months later Erin told me what happened. She had had other "spells" the week before her collapse in the ER. The rapid heart beating occurred after smoking and always stopped minutes later. She put it to the stress of the ER job and smoking, neither of which she wanted to quit. She didn't want to have it checked out either, hoping it would get better with time.

After the latest episode in the ER, she was scared and did go to a cardiologist at East Carolina University Medical Center. Erin had a cardiac catheterization that showed normal coronary arteries. After that test was performed, the doctors recommended she undergo an ablation procedure to cure her of the troubling tachycardia. Ablation meant destroying the abnormal cells that precipitated her very rapid heart rate episodes.

She explained that they wheeled her into the electrophysiology lab, like an operating room. She was sedated, and the interventional cardiologist gave her a local anesthetic shot and made a small cut over Erin's femoral artery in the groin.

The doctor then passed a special catheter, thinner than a pencil tip, up her femoral artery into the heart. The cardiologist then threaded the catheter through the heart's chambers up to the pulmonary veins. The pulmonary veins carry oxygen rich blood from the lungs back to the ventricles to be pumped out to the brain and body.

The tiny catheter was wire-guided by the cardiologist and sent EKG signals to a big TV monitor set up over the sleeping patient's head. The catheter placement was checked by fluoroscopy, an x-ray video, also displayed on that monitor screen. The tip of the catheter mapped the target area of abnormal cardiac cells by sending a small electric shock and recording the results on a computer hard drive. The electric shock was sent to stimulate the cells and start the atrial tachycardia in Erin's heart. When the cardiologist discovered the trigger site, he turned on a freezing element in the catheter tip to kill the bad cells, destroying the trouble spot forever.

Erin recounted, "The cardiologist told me it was 'shock, test, record,' for three hours. He told me he froze the cells he found that started my tachycardia. I had to spend the night in the ICU, but I think they fixed me."

Erin's Smoke Break

Erin had returned to the ER, stopped all heart medicine and was on a smoking cessation program recommended by her cardiologist. I knew she remembered seeing Kenny and me standing over her that early morning.

She smiled and said, "Doc, I'll be chewing some smoke-ender gum for my next cigarette break."

Chapter 29.
Do Dogs Know Grief?

Many ER nurses date or marry policemen or firefighters. They share the goal of helping others. In the small town of Williamston, North Carolina, population 5,844, those relationships are especially close. Most of the ER nurses have gone to school together with the boys and girls who become cops or medics. They maintain friendships over the years, becoming parents of children and raising them without locking doors in this close-knit community.

So, when the EMS radio called, "Police Officer shot. Code Red," the friendly banter in the ER stopped and the nurses looked at each other and at me. I took off my white coat, hung it over my chair back, and moved to the trauma bay. The long white coat might get in the way in the close quarters of the room used for critical patients. I always wore surgical scrubs and operating room sneakers at work. Years ago, I learned that wearing a dress shirt with a tie was a liability in the ER. As you recall, once I made the mistake of leaning over a psychotic patient and had to have the nurse cut my tie that he had clutched in his fist.

The term "Code Red" meant that the patient was bleeding heavily. It is every bit as ominous as "Code Blue," which indicated the patient was not breathing, often from cardiorespiratory arrest.

All of us scrubbed our hands with the brown, antibacterial liquid soap, dried them, and put on gowns and gloves. Nurse Sharon and Nurse Nancy, nervously opened the sterile surgical packs and put them on trays for easy access. The team was silent, each person mentally rehearsing. There was no talking, just preparation. They took out the intravenous supplies and turned on the heart monitor. Worry creased foreheads, glances were exchanged, then eyes were downcast. Then the nurses and I waited, our gloved hands by our sides, in anxious anticipation of what we knew would be awful.

The ambulance pulled up under the portico, the ER sliding doors banged open and the medics ran, pushing a stretcher to the trauma bay. The two paramedics, the ER nurses and I picked up the patient and transferred him from the EMS gurney to our stretcher. He was a big man, wearing a black combat uniform with a ballistic vest strapped on. There was no blood on his clothes or on the EMS stretcher. He was alive and moving his arms and legs purposely. His eyes were open but sightless. He didn't respond to the questions the nurses asked. I felt a faint pulse in the right carotid artery in his neck. There was a slight sheen of sweat on his face and his hands were cold to my touch.

It was evident that he had lost blood and his circulation was failing. Nurse Nancy removed the heavy vest and began cutting off his clothes with large trauma shears. I started a large bore in his right arm and ran IV with saline full speed. I moved around the stretcher to the patient's left side and started a second intravenous line. I hoped to quickly replace blood lost with saline to increase his volume and improve his blood pressure. It takes a blood bank thirty minutes to do a full crossmatch of the patient's blood to prevent a transfusion reaction. In this life-threatening hemorrhage crisis, I ordered type-specific blood to be set up for transfusion. I sent his blood sample to the blood bank for typing only. I knew that the full crossmatching would take too long.

He was in blood loss shock. His heart, brain, and kidneys were at risk. For survival, patients must be returned to normal blood volume within the "Golden Hour." That's the hour after injury and it is critical. If the patient can't be resuscitated in that time, the outcome is grim.

He had no obvious bleeding wounds and only a small bloodstain in his left armpit, just above the side vent of his bullet-proof vest. When I put my stethoscope on his chest I heard a very faint heartbeat, then nothing. His carotid pulse was still. I started chest compressions and asked the nurses to use the football-shaped Ambu bag to push air into him.

Two surgeons came down from the OR in their scrubs and were working with me to save him. The hospital grapevine had summoned them here. I had not had a spare moment to call them; they just showed up.

I had dumped four liters of saline and two units of blood into him and done chest compressions for forty-five minutes with no return of life. The surgeons agreed that taking him to the operating room would be futile. I ordered the CPR to stop, he was dead. The room was silent. Nurse Sharon was crying softly, and Nurse Nancy held her. I felt terrible. The surgeons and I looked at each other and just shook our heads in a sense of failure.

Everyone in the ER knew this officer personally. He was married to Nurse Sharon's sister. One of the housekeeping ladies was his cousin. His brother was a Highway Patrol officer who brought in a drunk driver to the ER the night before, and we had coffee together waiting for the blood alcohol test.

Nancy pulled me aside and told me that Officer Jim Hardison left a wife and three young children. Nurse Sharon continued to sob, sitting at the nurse's station in the ER.

I covered Jim's body with a sheet. Nurse Nancy and I moved his body into one of the cubicles away from the trauma room. The room had to be cleaned and made ready for the next emergency. Nancy and I kept busy picking up empty packaging from the floor, discarding the paper spooling down from the heart monitor, and putting anything with blood into the red contamination trash container. We changed our gloves and washed down the stretcher with antiseptic and mopped the floor, the water in the bucket was pink. Finally, with no more busy work to distract me, I snapped my gloves into the trash and left the room.

I sat down at my desk to type up a note on the emergency medical record, looked up and saw uniformed officers in the ER hallway. The State Highway Patrol and the State Bureau of Investigation officers were here to investigate the death of Officer

Jim Hardison. Both officers knew Jim and had worked with him many times. They had interviewed the other policemen in Jim's unit and came to the ER to compete their report of his shooting and death.

Nurse Sharon and I heard what they had discovered, "Sharon, we are very sorry for your loss. Jim was part of the county SWAT team in an operation to arrest known drug dealers. The dealers were in a meth lab set up in a farmhouse. Jim's team surrounded the property and called for them to come out and surrender. Multiple gunshots rang out from the farmhouse. A bullet hit Jim, in his armpit, just an inch above his protective vest. His teammates called 911."

"All the drug dealers continued to shoot at the police, who returned fire."

"Jim was the best of the best and we are very sad to be here."

The officers took copies of our records, thanked us and left. Nurse Sharon had dried her eyes and told me that she wanted to complete her shift rather than go home. Nurse Nancy and I looked at her and nodded.

The ER was very quiet when another police officer brought the dog in. It was a German Shepherd, pulling hard on the lead, looking around, sniffing loudly. The officer told us that he and Jim were canine officers as well as SWAT team members. We all looked at each other as he led the dog through the ER, back to the cubicle.

The dog began whimpering and moaning. We heard the dog's

paws scratching on the floor as it was walked around the dead body of her master, Jim. The nurses wiped the tears off their faces. I turned away from them, felt the private sense of loss and blotted my eyes, too.

After several minutes, the officer walked the dog down the hallway.

"Jim's dog needed to see his body. Needed to know he was gone."

As the officer walked with the dog out of the ER, passed through the doors to the ambulance bay, I knew then that dogs felt loss and grief, just like Sharon, Nancy, and I did.

Chapter 30
Come Dance with Me

The lady's husband and my wife encouraged me onto the dance floor when the band began to play. Mrs. Albright was a very petite woman and an excellent dancer, she looked at me and said, "Come dance with me."

She and I took a few spins around the floor and heard the clapping of hands. She smiled up at me and I grinned at the crowd around us. The event was an anniversary celebration, a festive time marking her first year of survival.

I remembered that time in the ER, as we rejoined our spouses at the bar. Mr. Albright raised his champagne glass and said, "Here's a toast to my wife and the doctor who saved her one year ago!"

We all toasted that, and Mrs. Albright and I shared a smile as we sipped the bubbly.

Last year, the Albrights had been on that very dance floor, enjoying the evening with friends when she collapsed at the dinner table. I was on the night shift in the ER when the radio announced, "Unit one to base, cardiac arrest, CPR, two minutes ETA."

The medics were doing CPR as they brought in the patient, so small that I thought it must be a child. The medics told me that they were called to the Country Club by the family when the patient suddenly fell over, and they arrived within three minutes of the 911 call. They found the patient on her back on the floor, not breathing or moving. The cardiac defibrillator paddles pressed to her chest showed ventricular fibrillation, the heart muscle unable to contract normally, usually a lethal condition. The medics pumped her chest, started an IV, and shocked her heart twice. They administered epinephrine, a drug to stimulate the dying heart, and began transport. They did get a faint pulse, a hopeful sign of heart action, but it stopped in the ambulance, as they pulled into the ER bay.

The ER nurses and I moved the woman from the EMS stretcher, continued CPR, and connected the EKG leads to her chest. On our trauma bay stretcher, I saw a few normal heart beats on the cardiac monitor followed by a barrage of premature ventricular contractions, a sign of electrical irritability of the heart, and a prelude to chaotic ventricular fibrillation and death.

I applied the paddles to her chest and shocked her. I hoped to stop the irritability of the heart and I succeeded. I began to sweat as I saw the monitor now showing a straight line. I knew I had just killed her. That sick guilty feeling lasted a few seconds, then I swallowed hard. I had work to do, with no time for self-pity or remorse.

The ER nurses did not hesitate and began chest compressions. I called for the airway bag, which contained intubation equipment and drugs. I told them not to stop the chest compressions as I opened the patient's mouth, inserted the laryngoscope into her mouth, careful to avoid hitting her teeth, and with the metal spoon-shaped shaft lifted her tongue up and out of the way. Between chest wall jumps from the chest compressions, I advanced the flexible clear endotracheal tube past her tongue, down past her voice box, and into the trachea to give oxygen directly to her lungs. I secured the endotracheal tube, fastened the football-shaped Ambu bag and pumped oxygen into her lungs. I prayed that the oxygen would help.

The patient's skin lost the bluish tinge of hypoxia and became pink, a sure sign the oxygen helped. But the cardiac monitor was a straight line, no heart action.

I ordered more epinephrine and continued chest compressions and oxygen by Ambu bag. Still no heartbeat, the monitor didn't change.

A nurse whispered to me that the relatives were here and she had shown them into the small family room and closed the door. The trauma bay and that family room were only thirty feet apart and sounds of the resuscitation could be heard by the anxious relatives through the closed door.

I continued giving epinephrine intravenously several more times with no change in the cardiac monitor. Almost always that meant that the heart muscle was severely damaged, and the patient was dead.

I had that sinking feeling of dread, knowing I would have to go to those relatives with bad news. I prayed for a miracle, really a selfish prayer, but sincerely felt.

I had turned away from the trauma bay stretcher, and a nurse touched my arm.

The cardiac monitor now showed a normal heart beat and I ordered chest compressions to stop, to check for vital signs. I felt a strong pulse in the patient's neck and the nurse reported a low blood pressure. She had returned to life and I would not let her slip away. I started pressor drugs to maintain her blood pressure. I ordered respiratory therapy to bring a ventilator for her in the ER, to continue oxygen therapy.

Her heartbeats were stronger and louder in my stethoscope and she was beginning to choke on the endotracheal tube. That was a sure sign of a healthy brain, but she needed the tube. I gave intravenous Valium, after which she stopped trying to spit the tube out.

I called the cardiologist who took her upstairs to the cardiac catheterization lab to evaluate her coronary arteries, which had to have a blockage. The catheterization team was very experienced with critical heart patients, so I felt calm enough now to talk with her relatives.

The nurse and I opened the family room door and walked in. Her husband and grown son jumped to their feet as we entered the room. I had started to speak when her son interrupted me, and grabbed both my hands with his, "You saved mom's life, we heard all you did, thank you.'

I said to them that was a strong team effort, starting with the paramedics who knew what to do, the emergency nurses and now the cardiology department. Mr. Albright, eyes welling up, and speechless, shook my hand and wouldn't let go.

As I remember that celebratory dance with a patient saved from certain death by the combined efforts of the entire emergency care team, I felt it was the culmination of my career in the ER. All the years of study, the years of making life and death decisions, and those emotionally traumatic times when I had to tell strangers of death of loved ones, the many sacrifices of my family along the way, forged me.

Knowing all these things now, would I have chosen a career in the ER again?

Yes! I sure would, in a heartbeat!

Glossary

Ambu Bag - a football shaped rubber bag rescuers use to give oxygen to a patient. When the bag is connected to the airway, squeezing the bag helps the patient who has stopped breathing.

Attending Physician - an experienced doctor who is responsible for supervising and instructing the house staff (interns and residents) at a teaching hospital associated with a Medical School.

Betadine - an iodine containing antibacterial solution used to prepare a person's skin for a surgical procedure. It is dark brown and stains clothing. It is not uncommon to see brown spots on the intern's shoes after surgical clinic.

Coma - behavioral unresponsiveness to external stimuli. Changes in the mental state of an emergency patient are among the most difficult and most critical. The causes and treatments are a source of continuing lifelong study.

CPR - cardiopulmonary resuscitation. The rhythmic chest compressions with rescue breathing improves the outcome in patients who have suffered cardiac arrest.

CT - computerized tomography. Head CT is the standard test to detect strokes in the emergency department. X-rays of the patient are taken and manipulated by a computer to render internal organs in high definition.

DTs - delirium tremens. Medical shorthand for the dangerous syndrome seen when chronic alcoholics stop drinking. The patient hallucinates, is mentally confused, and may have seizures. If untreated, delirium tremens has a five percent death rate.

EKG - electrocardiogram. The most accurate and least expensive heart test. Twelve leads are attached to the patient's chest which go to the recording device. The device moves paper through the recording system at a uniform speed to record the electrical action of the heart. EKGs can be sent from a moving ambulance to the ER. If that EKG shows a heart attack, the ER can call a cardiologist to attend the patient. The inventor was a German physician, who called it electrokardiogram, hence EKG. It can also be *ECG*, the equivalent in English.

EMS - emergency medical services. The rescue squad called by the 911 system to respond to crises. Staffed by paramedics and firefighters with training in CPR and trauma care.

ER doctor - emergency room physician. A graduate of medical school who has completed an internship and residency in the specialty. Physicians must pass a six-hour written exam and all day oral examination to become board certified. Of the 32,000 physicians practicing in United States Emergency Departments in 2010, 17,000 were certified by the American Board of Emergency Medicine.

ER - emergency room. Shorthand for the modern Emergency/Trauma center. Now also referred to as the ED or Emergency Department. Personnel include specially trained Registered Nurses and nursing assistants, formerly called 'orderlies.' Other staff include the department administrator and the chief of emergency nursing. Secretaries, social workers, pharmacists, and housekeeping staff play important roles in the smooth operation of the emergency department.

ETA - estimated time of arrival. Radio call abbreviation from an ambulance transporting a patient to the emergency department. It gives the staff time to prepare to receive the patient.

Foley Catheter - shorthand for the flexible hollow tube that is passed through the urethra to the urinary bladder. The end of the tube inserted has a small parallel passageway for instilling sterile saline to inflate a bulb to prevent accident dislodgement. Named after Frederic Foley who produced the design in 1929.

Fully packaged - emergency medical services parlance for protecting a patient from further damage due to transportation. Usually includes a long wooden or fiberglass backboard, plastic neck collar, and Velcro straps to keep the patient safe from any movement which could cause spinal injury.

Gel Foam - absorbable gelatin powder product. Used in emergency surgery to stop bleeding from the surface of vascular organs such as the liver or spleen. Bleeding from those surfaces cannot be stopped with sutures or electrocautery. Current surgical science favors saving the damaged spleen in place if possible. Removal of the spleen increases the risk for overwhelming bacterial infection.

Golden Hour - the hour after a person has suffered major trauma. Emergency/Trauma centers working with first responders and helicopter evacuation have developed protocols to get the wounded to definitive care within the first hour of injury. Any delay after that first hour causes measurable decrease in survival of the patient.

House staff - interns and residents collectively. In the modern era, the interns and residents stay at the hospital only on their call nights for 24 hours. Originally, residents resided in the hospital for all the years of their training, many of these 'residencies' were for seven years.

H&P - history and physical. The initial clinical evaluation and examination of the patient by the doctor. All medical students learn how to practice medicine by perfecting this important first step in caring for another person.

IV - intravenous. Shorthand for the administration of blood or fluid to a patient through a vein.

Intern - the doctor's first year of training after graduating from medical school. The intern is teamed with other interns led by a resident. The residents and interns are guided by Attending physicians and surgeons. Also called PG-1, for first postgraduate year.

Locum Tenens - Latin for 'to take the place of.' Think of a substitute teacher and you have the idea. *Locums* assignments are offered to qualified physicians who have agreed to work for companies that contract with hospitals for part time coverage in their ERs. Most of these assignments are temporary, replacing a physician who is on maternity leave or on a vacation for a few weeks. The locums physician has to be a formal member of the hospital staff, requiring credential submissions and a full curriculum vitae.

Mayo Stand - removable instrument tray set on an adjustable stand with wheels. Originally used in the OR to position instruments for ease of use of the clinicians. Also used in the emergency department for the same purpose.

M.O.D. - medical officer of the day. The physician on duty in the emergency department of a military or Veteran's Affairs/Administration hospital. He or she makes the determination to admit or discharge emergency patients.

MRI - magnetic resonance imaging. Body scans using powerful magnets and radio waves. Especially useful for spinal cord and brain injury diagnosis.

OR - shorthand for the Operating Room. The modern surgical suite has all the technology and staff to assure the best possible surgical outcome. The operating surgeon may have another resident surgeon assist in the operation. Medical students may perform assistant duties in their education.

PET Scan - positron emission tomography. A nuclear medicine scan which is used to observe metabolic processes. Useful in evaluating cancer and its treatment.

Resident - a physician who has completed an internship and is in the next phase of training leading to becoming a specialist. The first-year resident, also called PG-2 for post-graduate, second year, supervises the interns on his team. He is responsible for all the patient care of his interns and helps them. Most specialties require the successful completion of several years of residency and passage of a grueling board examination. The physician who passes the examination is issued a diploma of board certification.

Retractor - stainless steel surgical instrument that allows the surgeon direct vision into the patient by moving aside the tissues. The Deaver retractor used in upper abdominal surgery is ten-inches long with a curved blade similar to a hoe and has an angled handle. It is usually held by a medical student assigned to the surgical service.

Saline - shorthand for the physiological balanced salt-containing solution given intravenously. Usually administered in plastic containers holding one liter (about a quart liquid measure).

Scut - routine or menial tasks often viewed as onerous by the medical students assigned that work by interns and residents. May include routine blood sample taking, wound dressing changes, delivering charts to the residents, and holding retractors during surgical operations.

Scrub in - shorthand for being assigned to an operative case. Before entering into the operative suite, paper shoe protectors, cap and mask must be donned. Then the hands and forearms must be scrubbed with antibacterial detergent and sterile scrub brushes for five minutes by the clock. The hands then are held together up in the air, allowing water to run down the arms and drip into the scrub sink. A sterile towel is used to dry any remaining water. As you enter the surgical suite the nurse holds your gloves open and you thrust each hand as far as you can into each glove. Next the nurse holds up your surgical gown and you push your gloved hands deep into each sleeve. The nurse pulls the gown tight across the back and knots the ties together. Now you are scrubbed in.

STAT - a diagnostic or therapeutic procedure to be performed immediately. Latin: *statim,* immediately.

Ultrasound - applying a transducer (sound generator and receiver) to the patient and getting real time images. The quickest and safest imaging for the emergency patient. In experienced hands the heart, blood vessels, and abdominal organs can be diagnosed at the bedside.

Ventricular fibrillation - a chaotic lethal arrhythmia. The main pumping chambers of the heart, the muscular ventricles become ineffective and are noted to be wriggling like a bag of worms. Also called "VF." Treated with counter shock with defibrillator.

Ventricular tachycardia - a very rapid heart rate, often with inadequate time for proper filling of the pump chambers. Very dangerous. Can deteriorate into Ventricular fibrillation. Treated with counter shock with defibrillator.

Hedley Mendez grew up in South Florida. He's a graduate of Tulane University, the University of Miami School of Medicine, and a Medical Internship at Jackson Memorial Hospital, Miami. Dr. Mendez served as a Flight Surgeon in the United States Air Force during the early 1970's before beginning his nearly 40-year career in emergency medicine. He became a diplomate of the American Board of Emergency Medicine and maintained board certification for over three decades, practicing primarily in the Hampton Roads area of Virginia.

During the final years of his career, Dr. Mendez practiced *locum tenens* medicine, providing temporary coverage in emergency rooms throughout Virginia and North Carolina. He retired in 2014, and he and his wife moved to Wilmington, North Carolina, to be near their son and his family.

Printed in Great Britain
by Amazon

35993112R00119